YOUR DOG'S HEALTH

YOUR DOG'S HEALTH

FRANCO CAVALERI, BSc NB

BIOLOGIC
PUBLISHING INC

This book is published by Biologic Publishing Inc.
688-2397 King George Hwy.
White Rock, British Columbia
V4A 7E9 Canada
www.biologicnutragenomics.com
or *www.biologicnr.com*

Editor: Susan Girvan
Design and Production: Jen Hamilton

Printed and bound in Canada by Friesens

Library and Archives Canada Cataloguing in Publication

Cavaleri, Franco
        Potential within : your dog's health / Franco Cavaleri.

ISBN 978-0-9731701-1-5

        1. Dogs--Health. 2. Dogs--Nutrition. I. Title.
II. Title: Your dog's health.

SF427.C38 2009   636.7'0893   C2009-900431-3

DISCLAIMER

The content in this book is based on scientific research but should not be used as treatment for therapy without a clear understanding of the nature of the health condition. As each case of disease is unique to the individual, a full review of the condition by a certified health care professional must qualify the treatment. The purpose of the literature is to expand the knowledge of both professional and health care recipient in order to present alternative and complementary choices that can be applied with the close monitoring by a health professional. Under no circumstances are these programs to be applied instead of medication or medical advice without first having consulted the prescribing professional. The athletic performance-enhancement strategies herein should not be applied unless a complete examination by a qualified health care professional has first confirmed that the health condition of the individual can support the enhanced metabolic performance.

CONTENTS

INTRODUCTION

The programs presented in this book about canine health and happiness represent the next level of understanding for nutritional therapies. It is the science of nutrients interacting with genetic signaling, also known as nutrigenomics. This area of study, which is the focus of my research and product formulation work, is based on the cells' capacity to interpret and act on genetic instructions and hormonal signals, referred to in some circles as cellular consciousness.

I began my research into nutraceuticals decades ago, focusing on performance nutrition. I embarked on a conventional university education program in nutritional sciences and biochemistry and integrated my personal interest in performance enhancement in sport into my studies. This work led me to study the intricacies of our DNA, which we now know is where many nutrients interact. In fact, this research has identified many points of modulation for these nutrients—nutrients regulate genetic activity.

The fruits of this research were applied personally to achieve elite international status in sport. The research from the lab work, wedded to a scientific training approach, led me to win after win in the sport of bodybuilding, culminating with the win in Los Angeles California of the IFBB North American Bodybuilding title. My research continued, and I began developing sports medicines for mass production and worldwide distribution-nutrient-based supplements and medicines designed primarily for performance enhancement and therapy for humans. I was soon winning formulation awards in the human health industry and, not too long after, I was inducted into the Canadian Health Food Association's Sports Nutrition Hall of Fame in recognition of my scientific and education work.

My research continues today and includes an initiative to improve the health of all family members-from infants to adults to family pets. The research done to establish human wellness products often stemmed from animal work. My need to understand the metabolic differences from one species to another in order to make sense of this research led me to apply the animal-derived formulations to benefit my own pets. As I became more involved in competitive sport with my dogs, I became an informal consultant for other dog owners. Eventually, I began presenting my research to and consulting with veterinary clinics to help treat some of their difficult cases. The results in this controlled environment were impressive.

Due to repeated requests, I started to produce formulations in bulk to address the most common ailments in companion animals. It quickly became too costly to just give away the remedies because the demand skyrocketed. I soon began mass production of the powerful formulations, and BiologicVET was born.

The nutrient-based formulations developed from this research consist of powerful therapies and disease-prevention strategies that you can rely on for your pet. The products are designed specifically for the metabolism of pets. Our companion animals have distinct metabolic needs that require specific dietary and nutraceutical formulations. They also have very different social and instinctive tendencies that influence their emotional state, which, in turn, affects their ability to tolerate illness. A basic understanding of these needs enables a better level of care that preserves our pets' health and vigor throughout a longer life.

Too many pet nutritional products on the store shelves today are relabelled products that were originally designed for humans. This strategy has been adopted by manufacturers who simply try to stick with conventional methods, but the conventional outcome is inadequate. In addition, most of what we feed our pets today is designed primarily for our own convenience. Their health is a secondary thought, and this includes most forms of supplementation. My goal is to change this trend and provide a scientific standard for products that suit the metabolic needs of the animals themselves-to shift the focus of the pet nutrition industry away from profit, convenience, and convention and make our pets' health the priority.

The nutritional strategies that are outlined in this book are based on the nutrigenomic science that I specialize in. Historically, most nutritional remedies worked because they had nutrigenomic activity, but the formulations did not capitalize on this activity because it was not as well understood as it is today. Now, multiple ingredients can be chosen to accurately target a gene system, and both health maintenance and therapy can be that much more effective. The result is a powerful pharmacology that works as well as a drug, without the side-effects.

It's much easier to control a pet's diet than it is to control the diet of a human patient. People must contend with misdirected cravings for the wrong foods and the temptation to live unhealthy lifestyles, plus their ability to act on those cravings and give in to temptation. These emotionally and subconsciously driven challenges make it difficult for people to stay with programs that can restore wellness. When it comes to pets, however, compliance rests with their human owner.

Your dog can live a long and healthy life. Sound nutrition is the best way to empower your dog's body with the potential to prevent illness and preserve health. This concise guide has been provided to show you how.

-Prof. Franco Cavaleri, BSc. NB

ONE

A DOG IN THE FAMILY!

Welcoming a dog into your household will change your life. New pet owners look forward to this change, anticipating the joy of companionship, a warm bond, and time spent having fun with a lively, healthy pet.

However, like most relationships, this outcome is not guaranteed—it takes work and some careful planning on the part of dog owners. The benefits of companionship, learning opportunities, protection, and assistance are well worth the effort. Pets help children learn about responsibility, friendship, and a unique perspective on life. A dog can teach all members of the family life lessons on unconditional love, patience, tolerance, and life balance. In addition, research shows that interaction between a human and an animal companion can normalize a person's blood pressure and heart rate, and calm their state of mind.

Dogs need their daily exercise and, rain or shine, they must go for their walk to relieve themselves and stimulate their senses. This routine will bring their human guardians off the couch and out for a daily walk too. Who needs a personal trainer when you have a dog? And it's great to have everyone commit to a daily walk together, supporting the physical and emotional health of the entire family.

GET TO KNOW YOUR DOG

You may have chosen your dog after doing research into the breed to find out its basic traits and likely personality, and perhaps you spoke with current owners. Or you may have gone to a shelter and found a loving companion from the gaggle of animals of mixed or unknown origin. Or your dog may have found you, as was the case with my terrier-shepherd Dexter, who showed up in my front yard one day with clear signs of abuse, including a fractured front limb. We bonded as he healed, and he is now a welcome member of our family.

Regardless of how you and your dog came together, get to know your companion animal. If you don't have a general book about the breed (or the dominant breed in the mix), invest in one. Alternatively, talk to a knowledgeable breeder to find out how your dog will likely develop, how to interpret its behavior and cues, what to anticipate in behavior, and how to manage it.

The breed matters because many dogs have been bred for specific traits that will affect your relationship. For example, dogs bred for hunting, tracking, herding, or prey chase, such as greyhounds, German shorthair pointers, border collies, and blue heelers, require a lot of yard room for active play and need to be exercised regularly in order to stay healthy.

If you have a greyhound, it can be docile, extremely gentle, and relaxed in a home environment, but it will need regular physical activity so it can stretch out and run. When walking one of these dogs, owners must be conscious of the dog's ability to see things from afar and their instant reflex to chase. If you're not ready when the chase reflex kicks in or at least in control of the relationship, you could find yourself on your back, being pulled by a dog running at full speed.

A heeler will actually nip at the heels of dogs, goats, sheep, cows, or even humans it's attempting herd. This formidable dog was bred to protect and drive cattle. Its instinct to nip may express itself when it's at play with children. Bringing a herding animal into a home where children run and play is tempting fate as the animal may not be able to resist its genetic programming. Strangers may perceive the behavior as aggression, putting the animal in danger of being confined or even euthanized. Knowing a breed's inclinations will help you work with the animal's instincts and prevent disaster.

Jack Russell terriers are another popular breed, and Diesel, my second dog, is one of these. They can be tenacious and strong-willed. As much as dogs in general have a genetically driven tendency to protect the pack, if challenged, this little guy behaves as though he's a mastiff. And maybe in his little mind, he believes it. Jack Russells tend to be a little more independent than other breeds and prefer satisfying their penchant to hunt and dig for vermin over satisfying the desires of their human companions. It usually takes considerable patience and training to get a Jack Russell to abandon its prey and follow commands.

Too often, family pets are chosen for the wrong reason, although it is true that cute puppies and wagging tails are hard to resist. If you don't know and fail to account for the tendencies of the breed when interacting with and integrating a new family pet, the relationship can fail. Additionally, if you don't know the basic instincts of the animal so you can train your pet properly, then you fail your dog as the family leader.

Above all, never forget that your dog is a dog. Its primary concerns revolve around food, territory, and its place in the hierarchy of the pack—which is your family. Dogs are sensitive to stress, changes in routine, and challenges to their place in the hierarchy of the household.

MAKE ROOM IN YOUR HOME

Like their human owners, dogs like to know which space is theirs and what to expect. Feeding routines, exercise routines, and sleep routines are generally good for everyone. In your plan to integrate your dog, accommodate these needs for routine and instinctive behavior rather than finding them exasperating. The first order of business is double-checking your pet-proofing, and the second is letting the dog know which spaces are his or hers and which are yours.

PET-PROOF YOUR HOUSEHOLD

Beyond your dog's primary concerns, it has a keen sense of smell and an eagerness to get to know your home and keep track of what's in it. You need to simply accept that when your dog is nosing, sniffing, pawing, and possibly tasting things in your home, it is merely doing what dogs do in order to find out about unfamiliar things.

In order to provide a safe environment for your dog, you will have to pet-proof your home. This includes locking up household cleaners and medicines. These chemicals should be stored in a secured closet and on a high shelf so that both a door and height pose challenges to access. The same precautions should be taken with sharp objects or easily broken objects. Keep them up high and possibly behind doors.

Garages must also be made safe for your pet. Even though your pet may not be allowed into the garage, be prepared for curiosity to lead your dog into the forbidden area. Keep all poisons off the ground and high, especially antifreeze or other chemicals that may contain highly toxic ethylene glycol.

Another potential hazard is the chemical agents commonly used in yards. You must change to non-toxic products in order to avoid spreading poisons in the places where your pet is likely to roam. Even if your pet does not have access to your front yard, use safe chemicals on your property because dogs can get out at one time or another to get their snoot into treated areas. Grass treated with poisons is a hazard, as are puddles where yard treatment products may pool after a rainstorm. (These are also hazardous to small children, which is an additional reason to avoid using them.) Beyond your own sources, be aware that poisons are hidden beyond your home: throughout neighbors' homes and garages, in street puddles and garbage cans, and in parks and on golf courses.

Objects that you don't want your dog to chew should be kept away until you and the dog have established the boundaries between its toys and your family's belongings. The dog's toys should be readily available to provide alternatives to slippers and couch legs. This is especially important for puppies. Keep items that belong to humans off the floor, and ensure the dog has toys available to play with. Be careful with toys when multiple animals are involved because they can become very possessive and protective of their toys. If conflict arises, take the toy away and allow supervised play time with both animals until they both realize it is a shared toy. In addition, these pet toys must be species- and size-appropriate so they cannot be swallowed.

COMMON POISONS AND TOXINS

The chart below notes some common substances pets may consume that can cause serious damage. While senior animals and very young ones are more vulnerable to various poisons, some substances are dangerous for dogs of all ages, particularly if the dog is small. Your pet has a fast metabolism that ensures the toxins reach organs and do damage very quickly. If your dog is eating nutrient-dense food with antioxidant supplements, it will have a better chance of withstanding the effects of some of the toxins listed below.

If you suspect your pet has had encounters with the following toxins, take your pet to a vet immediately to induce vomiting and to have the appropriate remedy administered.

TOXIN	IMPACT
Alcohol (ethanol in beverages)	• can induce pancreatitis; modifies pancreas activities; metabolic acidosis; or a drunk, disoriented state
Alcohol (methanol in perfumes, rubbing alcohol)	• can cause metabolic acidosis; central nervous system influence; organ damage
Antifreeze (contains ethylene glycol, which tastes sweet)	• ethylene glycol in larger quantities causes liver damage, kidney failure, and death; smaller quantities may result in slight damage to organs and the development of long term disease; can induce a drunk disoriented state just before the development of the grave phase • less than an ounce will kill a medium size dog
Chocolate (contains theobromine, found in higher levels in dark chocolate)	• theobromine causes hyperactivity, increased heart rate, restlessness, limb tremors, and diarrhea; can also cause death
Coffee, tea (contains caffeine)	• caffeine can cause hyperactivity, increased heart rate, restlessness, limb tremors, and diarrhea
Electrolyte drinks with sugar	• causes a serious spike in blood sugar and insulin
Garbage	• can contain small bits of plastic, chemicals, or toxins that can cause blockages or lacerations or damage organs
Grapes and raisins	• can cause serious damage to some dogs' kidneys • symptoms can include vomiting, diarrhea, abdominal pain and lethargy
Holly berries (contain a number of toxins)	• can lead to acute diarrhea, vomiting, weakness or collapse if a number of them are ingested
Milk	• can cause gastrointestinal distress in dogs due to their lactose intolerance
Mistletoe	• can cause stomach distress and repeated vomiting, and lead to dehydration
Non prescription drugs (acetaminophen and aspirin) and prescription drugs	• Drugs intended for humans are not formulated for the smaller bodies and fast metabolism of the average dog. Inappropriate medication could result in organ or nerve damage or worse.
Onions contain N propyl disulphide	• causes anemia and can be deadly in large quantities
Pesticides (including rat poison and organophosphate neurotoxins) and herbicides found in puddles and ditches beside farms and gardens or in poisoned rodents	• can contain organophosphates, which can interrupt the endocrine system and interfere with thyroid activity, pituitary function, and insulin efficiency • can make smaller pets very ill

Poinsettias	• causes skin irritation, plus vomiting and malaise
	• large quantities can kill a dog
Poisonous mushrooms	• the same poison that will harm a human will kill a dog more quickly
Tinsel	• not likely to be toxic, but can cause serious intestinal damage including lacerations and strain if you attempt to pull the material out
Tomatoes (the green parts of the plant are the most dangerous)	• can cause clumsiness, drowsiness, slow heartbeat, diarrhea
Treated rawhide	• not easily digested
	• could cause intestinal blockage if large chunks are swallowed

Keeping a dog safe from poisons takes as much care and attention as keeping a very young child safe from poisons.

YOUR HOME PET FIRST AID KIT

It's best to be prepared for the unexpected and have the essential tools available to treat the consequences of minor or major accidents so they don't develop into tragedies. A stable condition can quickly turn into a dangerous situation if basic treatment tools and instructions are not available.

The following checklist shows the basic items that should be in your Dog First Aid Kit. It should be permanently affixed to the side of your companion animal's crate and travel with your pet on car trips. Be sure to include the addresses and telephone numbers of a few veterinary clinics close to the common parks and areas you regularly visit. Also include the phone numbers of two 24-hour emergency hospitals so that no time is wasted when time is of the essence. With these tools and resources at your fingertips, you will be better able to act quickly and confidently in the case of an accident with your dog.

ITEM	USE
A few packet servings of food	
Antiseptic towelettes	
Benadryl	fast acting, short term antihistamine in case of unexpected allergic reaction
Doggy sweater	to circumvent development of shock upon experiencing trauma
Extra collar and lead	
Feeding/watering bowl	
First aid tape	
Hydrogen Peroxide	to induce vomiting in case of consumption of toxins; as antiseptic as well
Instant chemical COLD pack	
Instant chemical HOT pack	
Iodine	less intrusive sanitizing agent
Matches	to heat tweezers for tick removal; disinfect/sanitize
Needle nose pliers	removal of larger impalements that cannot be left in while en route to vet clinic
Oil of Oregano	natural antiseptic application
Oral syringes	for administering liquids
Package of cotton gauze	
Pooper bags	
Q tips	
Razor blade	
Rectal thermometer	
Rubbing alcohol	cleaning wounds
Scissors	
Sterile ear wash solution	
Sterile eye wash solution	
Thermal blanket	to circumvent development of shock upon experiencing trauma
Tweezers	removal of ticks, slivers/splinters and thorns
Vet Wrap 2" roll and 4" roll	wrap limb or body injury
Water bottle	
Witch Hazel Preparation	astringents to help stop bleeding injuries

CREATE A FEEDING AREA

Food is a key interest of all dogs (and their owners). Feeding should take place in the same area every day to provide consistency and certainty. (It should also happen at the same time every day. Chapter 2 deals with these details in depth.) Keep all of the animal's food and supplements in the same area to make feeding, supplementing, and watering easy.

If the process is cumbersome or difficult, the feeding procedure could be compromised when you're in a rush.

The food supply is another item that must be out of the animal's reach, especially if you have more than one animal. Food can cause rivalries and some unwelcome behavior. Diesel, for example, will stand guard over food he can't eat if it appears to be accessible, just to make sure Dexter can't get to it. Diesel weighs twenty-four solid pounds, which makes him a big Jack Russell. Dexter weighs seventy-five pounds, but Diesel won't back down when it comes to food. It could get ugly, and it has at times if a morsel of food has fallen from the family dinner table. The dogs know not to get close to that table when we're eating, but Diesel will eye the dropped food from afar and if Dexter's ears and eyes perk up when he spots the food on the floor, it's enough to start a growling match that only stops when I growl my command back and scoop up the piece of food. It's a terrier thing; the dogs generally get along well. Golden retrievers, on the other hand, may never express themselves in this manner.

CREATE A SPECIFIC REST AND SLEEP AREA

Family pets must know precisely where their own space is. Although my dogs spend the majority of their time free outside, they always have access to their own heated kennel run, which leads to a private, enclosed doggy den for more cozy shelter when it's required. This ensures they have a retreat in the wintertime or if they are distressed.

Inside the house, Diesel has his open crate set up in the laundry room, and nearby each has a sleeping pad. This way they have a choice: they can sleep on their separate pads or they can share one. If Diesel is feeling ornery, as he might at times, he can retreat to his open crate. The crate provides perfect housing and a sense of security. Dogs are den animals, and the crate represents a den-like structure. Most people believe the crate is a harsh, punishing dwelling, but for dogs it's a cozy, safe retreat unless they've had bad experiences associated with it.

Dogs need and appreciate a sanctuary to claim as their own. Find a quiet area of the house, and make their space easily accessible but away from the main traffic for those times when they need a break. Another pad could be placed where the family spends the most time for when the dog wants to stay with the family. These clearly designated spaces will also set the stage for training to keep the dogs off the furniture and on their approved bedding.

MAKE ROOM IN YOUR LIFE

Almost everything you do in your life will have an impact on the life of your dog. The career you choose affects how much of your time will be available to your dog. A career change often has a major impact on their lifestyle. If you get pulled into a busy day, the dog can lose out on quality time with you.

Time for pets can be difficult to manage as the household changes. Newborns added to the family create a huge lifestyle change. In our home, the arrival of our little boy changed the world of our companion animals in many ways. Life in general just seemed to go faster and faster, and they got to spend less time indoors.

If you commit to a dog, the dog will need your time as much as they need their space. Dogs are social animals. We have bred them to enjoy human company rather than their fellow dogs, and we must take the time to socialize with them daily. And yes, they love regularity. Schedule your time with them, whether it's a walk, run, wrestling, hide-and-seek, or a game of fetch. If your canine companion gets extra sessions beyond what you've scheduled, that will be a bonus.

Mental stimulation is just as important as physical stimulation. Giving your dog a riddle to solve can be very satisfying. The riddle might be in the form of a ball with a delicious treat at its center. It will require a bit of physical and cerebral ingenuity to extract the reward. Keeping your dog mentally and physically occupied when you can't be there all day is critical to the dog's emotional health. If you don't keep the dog stimulated, the dog will amuse itself at your expense.

ARE TWO DOGS BETTER THAN ONE?

If you don't have much time for your companion animal, sometimes it's a good idea to introduce a second dog into the family. However, this decision requires consideration. You must still be an active part of the dogs' lives. The introduction of a second animal must be done carefully, especially if the first one has been part of the family for some time. Be aware though, that once the two dogs form a bond, they might collaborate to engage in elaborate schemes that will have you shaking your fist in frustration. You will likely establish a new respect for their intelligence.

In fact, if you fail to interact with the two dogs regularly to maintain your place in the social hierarchy, the dogs will form a subgroup that will be harder to manage. This subgroup of the family will go about their business, setting their own leadership structure despite your guidelines. Trying to call back two dogs on the prowl after they've gotten out of the yard is often more difficult than reeling in one. The pack instinct and competition for prey between them can send them far away. If you ensure you have control of the first animal before introducing a second one, it will help to demonstrate what is expected to the newcomer.

WHO'S IN CHARGE?

Wild dogs live in packs with designated alpha male and alpha female leaders. It is a rigid social structure. Domestic dogs live in human households with alpha males and females. To the family dog, this is the pack. If no one takes these alpha roles, the family dog may instinctively take them on, knowing that the family needs leadership.

As noted earlier, knowledge of your dog's breed is important. This will tell you whether your dog will tend to be more dominant or submissive. Your dog's personality will also either reinforce or undermine this breed tendency. A Jack Russell is relatively independent, while a golden retriever has been bred as a companion. In addition, dominant or submissive behavior can be outwardly expressed in very different ways from one breed or personality to another. For example, the Rottweiler, German shepherd, Doberman, Staffordshire terrier, and mastiff are breeds that guard and protect. A dominant personality of any one of these breeds could be a difficult animal to manage even by the family members. This animal may strive to be the leader or simply be less complacent than a dog with submissive traits or personality. This type of animal needs stern and firm direction and commands. "Stern and firm" must be carefully balanced, however, because a forceful approach used on a dominant animal of this breed can also provoke a fight.

Most breeds, regardless of breed role, have been bred to submit to man. However, even in the case of a submissive dog from a docile breed like golden retrievers, submission is often only extended to a limited few—only to those they believe to be above them in the hierarchy. Animals with a dominant tendency might even perceive the act of eating their food near the family dinner table as a sign of equality. Taking food from your plate to treat your dog could be interpreted as an act of forfeiting your food to a more dominant family member.

Allowing this dominant dog to sleep in your bed can also send a mixed message about the family (pack) hierarchy. The floor positions him distinctly lower than you on the 'Totem pole' leaving little room for interpretation. The daily routine has built in checkmarks which you might never relate to while your dog sees signs of forfeited authority and forms assumptions which guide his or her behavior. Without knowing it you could be offering control and dominance to your pet.

When it comes to physical activity, your dog is learning social skills while interacting with litter mates and members of the family "pack." It is critical that your dog be able to distinguish healthy play from rough and dangerous play with other dogs and members of the family. Limits are established during play time. This is when dogs learn things like how far they can take their biting. A puppy will try to push beyond those limits (just like a small child), and consistent human guidance will be required to maintain preferred behavior. If these limits are not established early, it is important to instill them with appropriate correction when the line is crossed.

For example, Dexter is one of the gentlest animals I know. This intelligent bundle of muscle will modify his play intensity to meet the level I establish. If I play hard, he plays back hard. He'll engage in a strong game of tug-of-war to pull me off my feet and drag me if I allow it. However, as soon as I hand the end of the rope to my young daughter he defaults to gentle mode. He knows to do this, but if he gets carried away I let him know with a firm command in a growling deep voice, "GENTLE." If he does not comply, I stop the game abruptly. If he fusses or acts up, he might see the walls of his kennel for thirty minutes or so. Some might say that I am irresponsible for allowing him to play hard with me and then attempting to teach him to differentiate between me and my daughter. You need to evaluate your dog's capacity to make this distinction; if it cannot, then no rough play should be allowed.

An extremely dominant personality, for example, of a large protection breed such as a Rottweiler might view the win of that tug-of-war match as a step toward dominance in the pack. Each animal will interpret these scenarios and express themselves in slightly different ways, based on their breed characteristics and their individual personality traits. But deep down, they all have a similar instinct. A dog that has a tendency to strive for dominance will have to be treated with this in mind at all times. That dominant dog might also be protective of its own doggy bed and might challenge other animals or humans if they were to take some space on it.

That deep growl you elicit from your pet every time you take away food, bed, or toys or get too close to another family member is not as cute as some make it out to be. That growl could be a warning to stay away from what your pet thinks they own and have rights to over and above you. It indicates that your dog perceives you as a subordinate or is challenging your position in the "pack." (One must also take steps to rule out the possibility of hidden injury, pain or malaise.) Unless this hierarchy is immediately clarified, an altercation could arise when you least expect it. It's not a safe ambiguity for your animal. Take charge with the strategies outlined below and skillfully demonstrate who is in charge. If the situation has escalated to deep entrenchment by a stubborn animal, professional obedience and behavior training may be required.

Submission should be automatically offered to all humans in the family, and you need to make sure this is the case at all stages of the animal's life. An interesting fact to keep in mind is that whoever fills the food bowl is recognized by your pet as an important provider for the family or, from their perspective, "the pack." Therefore, the person in charge of feeding tends to get more respect from the animals. In order for each member of the family to be recognized by the animal members as superior individuals in the social structure, feeding duties should be shared.

The sharing of duties helps each human member stay in control of the pets, however, lack of planning can also result in mistaken over-feeding or missed meals. Designing a detailed feeding chart can help. Assigning and labeling one or two days of the week to each family member may help define the feeding protocol, with one individual always being responsible for checking the chart at the end of the day to ensure the feedings were not missed. This chart must include a check box for the food and a check box for any supplements and medicine. More detail means there will be fewer mistakes. It's a good idea to include a check box for water recycling as well. This is also a great way to establish teamwork in the family and shared responsibilities for pets.

The bottom line is that in order to create a safe and viable relationship within the family, human control must be established regardless of the breed. It sounds egotistical to assume complete control over an animal, but it will make the dog's world less stressful. The leadership position is established through regular interaction and reinforcement of social position, and this interaction doesn't have to be oppressive or violent. It can be done with regular play sessions and walks that incorporate correction and training.

During this time of connection, represent yourself in the social hierarchy. This may involve a five-or ten-minute session of training using the "sit," "stay," and "down" commands. Showing daily that you are in charge reinforces the social hierarchy and reminds dogs of their place. I refer to these sessions as social tune-ups.

Your dog will need these tune-ups regularly; the frequency will depend on the personality and breed type. If you are easy-going with your dog, you may notice a tendency to push limits further and further each day as the dog tests boundaries. My dogs are terriers, and this is in their nature more than it might be for a golden retriever. Their tune-up involves a brief on-leash session to correct them assertively and reset those boundaries and a longer wait in the "sit" position before allowing them to take their bowl of food. Repeat and test the commands with an authoritative tone. The tune-up can save grief by retuning your animal's attention and respect for your role.

If your dog is growling over a space in your home, whether it's a bed or a favorite corner, it could be a sign that the dominant role has become fuzzy. You must take full responsibility to parent your dog, using simple language the dog understands. This establishes position and will reassure and calm your pet.

If an animal gets out of control, expressing insubordination or unacceptable dominance, the leash training session must be applied daily—even if it's only for ten minutes—until the social structure is made clear once again. Walk the dog in zigzag formations while he or she stays close to your side—left side preferably. A professional can help you perfect this leash education. The dog MUST respond to your direction and you must continue this process until the dog does. Each family member should engage in this process to establish their position in the hierarchy and train the animal to obey their commands while on the leash. If you are using the "snap" correction method, it must be done in a safe and considerate manner. Softer, smaller animals will need an extremely gentle snap, while others may need a more assertive jolt. Don't let your dog pull you around on the leash. If the leash tension tightens, the snap will correct the problem. Pulling back to meet your dogs pulling force can make for the tug-of-war challenge. The snap in the direction you intend to take gives you the advantage. Your dog has the advantage being low to the ground, when you engage in the pulling match; every time you lose, your dog is leading you and is walking you. A loose lead means you are in control; you are in the dominant role. A tight lead means he or she is leading the walk. Always be careful to prevent neck injury and respect the fact that the neck and throat are very vulnerable body parts that can be easily injured. The vulnerability of the body part is the factor that gives you control with that snap method. Respect it.

Although diverting your pet's misbehavior is the best way to train, scolding your pet is not a bad thing. Your dog should know when it has done something wrong, but it must also be made aware of what is correct at that very moment. If your dog chews your slipper, for example, it should receive a firm and emphatic "NO!" when it is chewing the slipper. Don't scold ten minutes later when the dog is in another room because most animals will not be able to make the connection. The alternative dog toy should be made available immediately upon delivering the firm negative message. Offer praise when they accept and use the preferred toy or activity. In addition, be aware of your dog's decision to play with the right toy instead of the slipper in a subsequent occasion. Offer positive reinforcement in the form of a treat for making the right choice.

Bear in mind that some dogs need firmer correction than others. Some are so sensitive they need only a mild suggestion; a firm, loud correction for these sensitive animals could result in emotional distress. Your discretion is crucial. Look for the signs when you bark out your correction, and tone down or crank up your intensity to get the job done in a healthy way. Don't be intimidated by the challenge of getting it right. However sensitive the personality, your dog will eventually forget the scolding and appreciate the alternative choice. And scolding does not mean beating. Firm assertive correction that may involve physical restraint might be in order, but always express, unconditional love just as they will! The best training is interceptive whereby you notice what they are about to do and provide the alternative or prevent the action before they lunge into it. This type of correction provides two lessons: it demonstrates the preferred action, and it reinforces your dominant position in the relationship. This interceptive process teaches the animal to look to you for guidance in the future before jumping out suddenly into danger.

Dogs will gravitate towards taking away your control; it's a natural tendency, especially for puppies. Puppies or young adults are constantly trying to find their place in the pack. If you are not in control as alpha, simple tasks such as clipping their toe nails, application of ear medications, cleaning their teeth, and trimming their coat or a visit to the vet or wound treatment if they are injured might become challenging. If they establish a dominant position or an emotionally unstable state, you cannot expect them to conduct themselves in a respectable and expectable way in public—a public designed primarily for humans.

Leading the pack requires that you clearly define your position on a regular basis, and you learn to read your dog's body language. When you ask your dog to do something with a clear one-word command, and it complies, you are both confirming who's in charge. Teaching your animal to respect your wishes is critical to its wellbeing. First of all, your praise and rewards build confidence and character. Secondly, being able to control your pet ensures you can keep it safe. If your dog does not respond to your commands, it could run into traffic or eat something poisonous despite your commands. Your alpha control should keep your dog from reacting unexpectedly because he or she should be reacting to your commands and not his or her rationale or environmental triggers.

DOGS COMMUNICATE THROUGH SUBTLE SIGNS

Dogs communicate primarily in sign; more accurately in body language and scents. They will demonstrate submissive activity by rolling onto their backs and exposing their bellies. The belly-up position is offering you a sign that they except you as dominant, but don't allow children to jump on and take advantage of this compromised position because it could evoke an unexpected reaction. Respect the offer. Know what it means to your pet. It's a delicately vulnerable position to them.

Successful communication is key to mental and emotional stability for your animal and if they are able to convey their intentions they are more likely to be content and emotionally stable and therefore, physically healthy. Most importantly it's crucial for these messages to be understood by the human family members in order for the relationship to stay healthy.

The body language and other related communication methods these animals use are not too far off what we humans use at a subconscious level. If a man walked straight at you, shoulders and head held high and eyes glaring straight into yours your first reaction might be defensive and if your personality was dominant or aggressive your subsequent reaction might be a glare straight back. The one who turns away may lose that first challenge for dominance in relation to that instance. This is how it works for dogs as well.

Submission or lack of aggression in humans is expressed as it would be in our pets. A person walking with their head down and body hunched over may not necessarily be showing a submissive personality, but they are definitely avoiding eye contact and challenge. I've seen people yawn in the face of adversity or uneasiness. Dogs do the same thing. A yawn while looking away is an attempt to avoid confrontation. Lip-licking may be an attempt to cover the teeth to avoid confrontation; the opposite of exposing the teeth in a demonstration of aggression. Exposure of the teeth accompanied by a growl is a warning: "Beware, I might bite if you don't comply!" A dog that yawns and licks its lips in response to an assertive correction is recognizing your command as the final word, or it simply fears your tone. This animal may not need such firmness in future training.

As much as I know my dog Dexter to be thankful of the rescue, he'll test me once in a while to see how far he can go in the pack. Keep in mind that our pets view the entire human and animal members of the family as their pack. This is the same for our cats where the pack equivalent is called the clowder. Occasionally, Dexter will stand on the patio chair and stare me straight in the eyes. He'll bring himself to my eye level and face off with me. This isn't necessarily a bad thing. However, when this stance is accompanied by the other body language that indicates an aggressive attitude, action must be taken by the human leader of the pack.

Dexter will stand on the patio chair knowing he's not supposed to be on the furniture in the first place! Our pets are more aware than you might think, and when they are not consciously aware they are subconsciously driven by those instincts. Although, he is very respectful of our relationship, instinct causes him to do things he may not consciously plan. Diesel is similar, only Diesel, the Jack Russell, is more prey-driven, and his weakness is this irresistible instinct to chase and kill vermin.

Here was Dexter, three feet in front of me, his eyes wide open, ears pointing forward and up, tail up, his front paws on the back of the chair to elevate his head to my head height and his back legs on the seat. Diesel was watching intently from the sidelines as I approached; he sensed the tension, and rushed away to avoid getting caught in the crossfire. Dexter, my bigger dog, followed me with his head as I approached him at the chair. At that instant, I turned to face him squarely, widened my eyes as big as they go to match his, and firmly with a drawling scowl that sounds like a growl I commanded, "NO! Dexter OFF!" Before I could finish "NO!" he flew off the chair, and, looking down at the ground and away from me, he slowly walked past me licking his chops.

The detailed description of body position and mannerism presents many of the physical signs of the animal's intention and state of emotion. Heed these signs as indications of what is going on in your pet's mind, and keep them in your mind as you guide your canine companion.

The dangerous alternative to what happened with Dexter is that he might have added a growl with teeth showing and raised hair on his neck and back while staring me in the eyes. That would have been a different situation altogether and could have ended badly. But that is not Dexter; I know him well enough that it could not ever reach that end with me. However, if Dexter were to be in a different family environment, where his dominant tendency was allowed to progress, who knows what could come out of it in due time? These are the signs that must be acknowledged; these tendencies should be discouraged before the animal gains the wrong impression.

Diesel's fear and attempt to escape in this situation even before I turned to face Dexter might be confirmation that Dexter's motive was, in fact, a challenge, although meager. Diesel sat to the side with his right paw off the ground looking down at the ground and away with an eye on the action. They know when trouble brews in the family unit; they sense our emotional state by the way we humans present our own body language without being conscious of it. They can also smell various secretions associated with some of these states. Each one of Diesel's and Dexter's actions, as small as they seem, have significance from the "look away and down to the ground" to the lip licking and single paw off the ground. These are all signs of submission or at least avoidance of conflict or challenge. Looking away ensures no direct eye contact; licking the lips hides the teeth from showing as an accidental threat, and the paw off the ground demonstrates physical instability—the opposite of an intimidation attempt. For many, this scenario would have amounted to the dog climbing on the furniture and nothing more, failing to understand the nature of the situation from the animals' perspectives.

If a strange dog, such as a physically strong breed like a Staffordshire Bull Terrier, German Shepherd, or Rottweiler, had challenged me in this way, I would not have taken the chance to face off. I did so because I know my own pet, and I know what needs to be done to maintain a healthy and safe relationship at home.

Dog language is rather basic when you know it. A dog mounting a child, for instance, might be demonstrating dominance over the child. You or the child may not know that with this action a new family structure has been or is being established from the dog's point of view. This needs to be corrected before the child climbs on the dog during play; this mounting by the child may be perceived by that same dog as a challenge for repositioning in the social hierarchy. An understanding of basic dog language and social interaction will prevent tragedy. Dogs mount other dogs, regardless of gender, to show dominance over the mounted. A dominant dog may jump at a child's challenge to nip or even pin the child for reasons we may never be able to understand unless this language or the basic social instincts are understood. Putting your dog in his or her place from puppyhood onward will make clear to them where they stand in the family structure and where they do and do not have authority.

CHECK YOUR DOG REGULARLY

I use my hands, particularly probing fingers, to pat and explore my canines' bodies from nose to tail approximately every second day. I may do this as they feed or immediately after feeding. This routine can also be incorporated into the regular brushing that should be done a few times a week. It's important your dog become accustomed to this handling from puppyhood.

It wasn't too long ago that I found a tooth puncture in Diesel's shoulder, an obvious sign of a brief battle between Dexter and Diesel. If you find a tooth puncture on one side you're likely to find other bruising or punctures from the bottom jaw somewhere else. Part the hair to feel the site and look down to the skin. I've found tooth punctures a few times in the past on both of them.

In the case of this particular shallow puncture into the muscle, it was not a dangerous matter as it did not penetrate too far. However, if it gets infected and inflamed underneath, the infection can travel to cause serious health consequences. Catching these injuries early by regularly feeling for them helps avoid tragedy. If you are unsure of the age, treatment protocol, or severity of the wound, see the vet right away in case there is underlying infection.

In the case of Diesel's puncture, I simply pulled the scab off the puncture site every day and dabbed the surface aggressively with a diluted solution of oil of oregano and olive oil. If the scab seals the wound, it can trap infection that can progress unnoticed. Within a week this puncture was healed.

The oil of oregano provides topical antiseptic activity, but Diesel's nutrient-dense diet supplemented with extra biologically active vitamins, minerals, and phytoantioxidants empowers the immune system from within to clear the tissue damage and potential microbial invaders.

Oil of oregano delivers powerful antibacterial, anti-parasitic, and antiviral activity all in one. It's great to have around the house for the human and animal members of the family. However, keep it out of the eyes and ear canals as it can irritate as well.

Your canine first-aid kit should also include an emetic such as hydrogen peroxide to induce vomiting when your pet has consumed something poisonous. (You may feel that your dog is capable of vomiting without any help from you, but there will be times when you want to get the substance out of its system quickly.)

Check eyes and ears every day. An infected eye that is allowed to fester can result in blindness in very little time. Ears can be a site of ongoing distress for unhealthy animals. The ear is a perfect environment for tick and mite infiltration, and ear mites are one of the more common reasons for veterinary visit. Regularly inspect the ears to make sure they are clean.

Closely inspect the teeth and gums. Smaller breeds of dogs are more vulnerable to tartar or calculus build-up because their smaller teeth tend to have tighter folds and crevasses. Regular feeding of raw chicken necks can prevent the build-up. Cooked chicken necks or other bones will not and are an emphatic no-no.

Pay attention to regular sneezing and snorting, which may be a sign of respiratory illness. In this case, a veterinary visit is required immediately. And last, but not least, look at your animal's excrement regularly. Make sure it's formed and void of worms.

You need to do a quick visual check daily and engage in a regular closer inspection of your pet, using your fingers to massage the entire body at least three times a week. This is a bonding and relaxation time, but it also allows you to find ticks, nodules, and other dermal growths. Regular and thorough inspections of your family dog are essential in order to avoid serious health problems and expensive veterinary bills.

CHOOSING A VET

Your little companion depends on you to look after vital issues relating to health. The chapters that follow will guide you in ways to nourish your dog and keep it active and healthy. However, despite your best intentions, accidents will happen, as will the occasional illnesses. The treatment you choose and the strategies you use to restore your dog's health are up to you. Inform yourself, and be an active part of your dog's healthcare along with your veterinary doctor. The doctor treating your dog will be happy to have you participate by taking notes so you can give accurate details about any problems and comply with agreed-upon treatment suggestions.

If you're unsure about some medical facts, ask questions to better understand why a particular treatment is needed. Ask how complementary strategies such as nutrient-based programs can improve on treatment and long-term maintenance of health. If you prefer to do some research on the Internet before making a final decision on how to proceed, be certain that your sources are scientifically referenced or otherwise credible. Complementary healthcare can involve conventional drug applications alongside natural remedies to provide better results than drugs alone can deliver. Drugs often treat symptoms, but if the metabolic cause of the symptom is not corrected, the disease cannot be cured. Metabolic correction usually supplies missing nutrients so the body can heal itself. These health corrective strategies will be discussed in more detail in Chapter 5.

The veterinary doctor who monitors health and treats disease is your choice. If your current pet healthcare provider is not working out, it is your responsibility to get involved, ask questions, make suggestions, and voice your concerns. Just because the veterinary clinic is located around the corner doesn't mean it's the best fit for your pet. Some clinics have doctors who specialize in particular breeds or species. Others will specialize in methods of treatment such as naturopathics or alternative treatments. Take the time to research the different professionals in your area and find the best fit for your species, breed, and your philosophies.

INSURANCE

Taking good care of your dog is good insurance, but you may want to consider pet insurance, particularly as your dog ages. Talk to other owners to assess the various products out there.

VACCINATIONS

There is no doubt that vaccinations are controversial, just as there is no doubt that both human and pet populations have benefited from the practice. It is clear that vaccines are not entirely harmless, but they do protect populations. Human cases of polio and smallpox have disappeared, and cases of parvovirus and distemper are rarely found in domestic dogs. The questions about vaccination are really about how often they are required and which ones are required. Many pet owners are wondering if an annual booster shot to boost an immune system that is already loaded is a good thing. Others are questioning the effects of the preservatives used in the preparations.

Once your pet has been vaccinated to establish early immunity, immunity can be maintained by a healthy diet that contains vitamins, flaxseed lignans, essential fatty acids, and fibre.

Timing: In the early weeks of life the immune systems of puppies may not be mature enough to trigger an appropriate response to a vaccination. The best way to protect them is to keep them in a clean environment and away from contact with disease. The immunity animals are born with and mother's milk provides will fade at around three months; before that time, the animal's natural immunity will interfere with the vaccines.

Shots: All-in-one shots can overburden the immune system. The following schedule offers safe protection and allows the immune system to react to the invaders one at a time.

VACCINE	AGE
distemper	3 to 4 months
parvovirus	4 to 5 months
rabies	according to local requirements, without overlapping with other vaccinations

When it comes to considering a booster shot, use a **Titer test** to determine if your pet's blood is carrying sufficient antibodies or antigen recognition before you decide to get one.

Alternatives to Vaccines: Nosodes are homeopathic preparations made from tissue, pus, blood, or saliva from an infected animal. The remedy is then diluted using homeopathic standards. Some veterinary professionals use this type of complementary or homeopathic protocol. Animals with known autoimmune conditions such as lupus can benefit from receiving nosode immunizations.

TWO

GOOD NUTRITION FOR A HEALTHY DOG

Canines are mammals—just like their owners. Like humans, dogs need food packed with nutrients rather than empty calories. They need digestible sources of vitamins and minerals. They need the right proportion of protein, fat, and carbohydrate to maintain a healthy body. And they need a supply of clean, accessible water.

Despite the theory that owners and their dogs eventually grow to resemble each other, there are some obvious differences between owners and pets. There is also a key, less visible difference: a dog's metabolism runs faster than a human's metabolism. In other words, your dog's body breaks down food to make energy, rebuild tissues, and produce waste more quickly than you do. A dog's heart beats faster than a human heart. A dog's cellular processes—including cell replication, restoration, and turnover—also happen at a faster rate. (All of this explains why your dog's body ages more quickly than yours does.) The pH of the dog's gastrointestinal tract, the probiotic flora, and the digestive enzyme distribution is different from the same factors in a human tract. In addition, a dog's digestive system is physically shorter than a human's and moves food and nutrients faster down its length.

These metabolic and physical differences may seem inconsequential, but the health implications for your dog can be profound. At a minimum, your dog requires canine-specific dietary profiles of protein, fat, and carbohydrate to supply the proper ratios of vitamins, minerals, and amino acids (from the protein) and fatty acids (from the fat). In fact, with an understanding of the impact of this distinct metabolism, you can easily improve the health and quality of life of your precious companion animal. High-quality food will work its magic on your pet's health and vitality quickly thanks to this faster rate of metabolic activity. A faster metabolism also means that poor-quality food will have a speedy negative effect, and deadly toxins can potentially harm or kill your dog more quickly than they can harm you.

WHAT MAKES A GOOD QUALITY PET FOOD?

Good nutrition is the foundation of your pet's mental and physical health. It's the foundation of a high quality of life and vitality, and it must be crafted to suit a dog's metabolism. The common dog foods in the marketplace are designed primarily for the owner's convenience, with optimal pet health as a secondary objective. This doesn't mean popular dog foods are bad for your pet, but it does mean that these foods may not supply all of your dog's nutritional needs. If your pet's health was the primary focus when pet food was being formulated, with no consideration given to convenience, then dry, boxed, or bagged pet food wouldn't be an option. Neither would the wet, canned variety. In our fast-paced world, however, convenience does matter. Your goal is to find a manageable way to feed your pet good-quality food given your lifestyle.

As you evaluate the food you give your pet, it's important to remember that feeding your dog and nourishing your dog are not necessarily the same things. Nourishing your dog depends on choosing pet foods based on nutritional qualities such as nutrient density, the bioavailability of the nutrients, and the ratio of protein, fat, and carbohydrate.

Nutrient density refers to more than protein, fat, and carbohydrate levels. In addition to the type of protein and the quality of the fat and carbohydrate, nutrient density takes into account the concentration of vitamins and minerals. A sprinkling of vitamins and minerals in a bowl of food that has significant amounts of carbohydrate filler (such as grains like corn) means the nutrition is low-density. Higher quantities of vitamins and minerals mean higher nutrient density. A food that is made with quality protein and vegetable sources and omits the grain fillers will present a higher nutrient density for your dog.

Read pet food labels carefully to evaluate and compare nutrient densities as best you can. Ingredients are listed in order of quantity on the package—those listed first are the most abundant. Dog foods with more fillers than nourishment will list ingredients such as corn, wheat, rice, or other grains first or near the beginning of the ingredient list. In fact, the only plant-based ingredients that should be in your dog's food are lower-glycemic vegetables such as spinach and squash and lower-glycemic fruits such as apples and pears plus a very few higher-glycemic vegetables such as yam, sweet potato, and carrots. These are the carbohydrate and other nutrient sources that can be moderately digested and reasonably managed by the dog's metabolism. Chopped flaxseed is a great addition. However, these ingredients should be lower on the ingredient list in your preferred dog food, and grains like corn and wheat should not be listed at all.

The majority of the feed ingredients, that is, the ingredients making up the beginning of the ingredient list, should be animal meats. Beware of words like "chicken meal," "lamb meal," or "beef meal." The term "meal" refers to a mash of non-specific tissue. Choose foods for dogs that describe the meat ingredients as "chicken muscle meat," "human-grade beef muscle meat," or "whole, bone-in chicken thighs/wings." This ensures that a quality ingredient has been selected as a major component of the feed. The protein in muscle meat provides a bounty of amino acids, vitamins, and minerals in their natural forms, as does the natural bone component.

Beyond nutrient density, the presence of a nutrient on the ingredient list doesn't mean it will be available for absorption after the food has been digested. The way the foods are processed by the manufacturer affects the **bioavailability** of the nutrients. This is a measure of how well or efficiently a body can metabolize (break down) and absorb the nutrients in the food. This measure of absorption is the basis for calculating the measure of retention of the nutrient in the tissues, which is the biological value. The biological value is the true measure of a food's effectiveness in your pet's body. If you have been reading about human nutrition and factors that affect human health, none of this information will be news to you, but often we forget that it applies to other animals, such as our pets, as well.

Pet foods can be so intensely processed to eliminate pathogens, "improve" flavor and texture, and enhance shelf life that the nutrient value and the bioavailability (and the biological value) of the ingredients that remain are seriously damaged in the process.

In other words, the label may indicate that an ingredient is in the product, but that doesn't mean it's available to the body after the digestive process. If you rank pet feeds based on bioavailability alone, the best form is raw, then comes home-cooked; then canned, wet food; and finally, dry kibble. (This is assuming that each food type being compared consists of the same ingredients.) The bioavailability of the nutrients in kibble is considerably lower than the bioavailability of nutrients in properly designed raw food. Generally, foods that are exposed to processing techniques such as high heat, oxygen, acids or alkaline solutions to "pre-digest" them, and intense light tend to have lower biological values because the bioavailability of the nutrients has been compromised.

Improvement in the bioavailability or biological value of the nutrients in an animal's food can give its body the materials it needs to maintain or restore health. Spontaneous healing through proper nutrition is not a miracle, especially if the illness is caused by a nutritional limitation. Nutritional limitation does not have to cause a clinical state of deficiency to result in a significant reduction in the effectiveness of your dog's immune system. Your dog does not have to be ill to be feeling and acting "sub par." You know the difference between feeling (and being) very well and feeling "draggy" when it comes to your own body. Your dog's body experiences the same states. Nutrient-dense foods with a high biological value can keep your dog well.

If you've been doing research on human nutrition, you will know that food with the **proper ratio of protein, fat, and carbohydrate** triggers a hormonal response in the body that is not limited to the release of the hormone insulin. The proper balance of nutrients elicits a cascade of a variety of hormones throughout the body, influencing the release of still more hormones involved in the management of energy and mood, brain activity, cardiovascular regulation, liver function, and the incidence of inflammation. This rippling hormonal response is the same in your pet.

The wrong ratio of protein, fat, and carbohydrate in a meal creates imbalanced hormonal responses throughout the body, interferes with insulin's ability to process sugars and transport and use fatty acids and amino acids, and can compromise health in pets. Because the vitamin, mineral, amino acid, and fatty acid needs of a dog are quite different from those of their guardian owner, the proportion and types of protein, fat, and carbohydrate in the dog's food must be different. Giving your dog human food or pet foods without a proper formulation strategy can throw their hormonal balance off. Your dog will not be as well and vital as it could be. And, eventually, your dog may become ill.

What is the right ratio? A good quality dog food will provide a minimum of 25 percent protein, with close to 15 percent dietary fat and around 5 percent carbohydrate/fiber. The rest of the food is made up of moisture. These proportions are not cut-and-dried and are a controversial subject. For example, puppyhood, which is characterized by faster rates of development of neurological tissue, bone, and muscle, requires larger quantities of protein and fat to accommodate the developing body's demands. The quality of this protein and fat also plays a huge role in how well these different levels are tolerated or used by the body.

THE ROLE OF PROTEIN

The protein content of dog feed has become a huge controversy among researchers. There is a misconception that a diet that is too high in protein can contribute to acidosis (increased acidity in the blood, which can lead to osteoporosis and, ultimately, kidney failure), as well as metabolic inefficiency. A mammal's body responds to acidosis by trying to neutralize the blood immediately. It extracts calcium and other minerals from bones to bring the body's pH (acid-alkaline balance) back into the normal range. The research shows it's not necessarily the quantity of protein that contributes to these problems. It is more likely to be the *quality* of the protein that causes the problems.

Protein supplies the building blocks for the immune system, cartilage, muscles, hormones, enzymes, and cell membranes throughout the body, including the brain, in the form of basic chemical components called amino acids. Many dry kibble foods have protein contents ranging from 10 percent to 35 percent. The problem with this protein isn't the quantity. The problem is that processed kibble and canned meat will contain protein damaged by processing, making it difficult for a dog's body to metabolize it. Poor quality or damaged protein is not able to deliver key amino acids that make it useful to the cells once the food is broken down. These amino acids may be present on the label, but glycosylation and denaturation, which are the result of processing, have damaged the amino acids so they are no longer bioavailable.

In addition, this damaged protein requires more processing by the body to filter out the non-usable and damaged amino-acid building blocks that do make it into circulation. This processing results in more urea waste that must be removed by the kidneys. Thus lower-grade protein requires more metabolic work, produces more waste, and also increases the dog's need for water. If the water needs are not met, there will be further pressure on the now hard-working kidneys. All of this extra work is required to process lower-grade protein sources that provide fewer usable amino-acid and fatty-acid building blocks.

The consequence of poor-quality protein is, therefore, hardship on the liver, kidney, and other systems involved in the elimination of metabolic by-products. When the stress on these systems is diagnosed in the form of liver or kidney disorders, the solution adopted—in error—is to lower the *quantity* of protein in the diet in an effort to ease the body's processing burden. A much better and more effective solution would be to raise the *quality* of the protein. A dog's foundation diet requires an abundant supply of undamaged protein in the form of meat that has not been subjected to intense processing.

Unfortunately, pet health professionals often advocate the use of low-protein feeds instead of focusing on the kind of protein the dog has been getting, going as low as 5 to 10 percent protein from animal meats for a dog whose diet should be mostly carnivorous. These are absurdly low protein levels. Reduced protein feeds undermine the entire biological system of the animal, limiting immune system function, antioxidant potential, energy levels, tissue repair, brain development, and coat and skin health. More canine-dietary protein research is posted at *http://www.biologicnr.com/2170.*

THE EFFECT OF CARBOHYDRATE SOURCES

When considering carbohydrate souces in your pet's diet, be aware that a dog's body breaks down complex carbohydrate in ways similar to the ways a human body does, however, evolution has not given their bodies the tools needed to use carbohydrate sources efficiently. Unlike humans, dogs (as well as cats) lack salivary amylase, the enzyme responsible for starting the digestion of carbohydrate in the mouth. Although dogs produce more of these carbohydrate-digesting enzymes in their small intestine than cats do, which equips them with a better ability to digest and use carbohydrate food sources, dogs cannot tolerate these dense carbohydrate sources the way humans can once carbohydrate overloads the circulation.

This means that dense carbohydrate sources in dog food—rice, corn, and wheat—can be digested and metabolized very quickly, and their sugar load is quickly released into the dog's bloodstream. This can contribute to blood-sugar spikes. Dogs are very sensitive to sugars in their systems. Sugars and the grains that can supply these sugars abundantly were never part of their evolutionary diet, and their bodies are ill-equipped to deal with the sudden blood-sugar elevations these ingredients can create. Insulin resistance is now becoming more and more common in household pets, and the higher glycemic- or carbohydrate-loaded diet—those grain-based fillers—is the primary cause.

The ultimate result of unchecked insulin resistance is diabetes, but pre-diabetic states that are rarely diagnosed cause all sorts of metabolic havoc and lead to the development of other illnesses. An insulin problem will interfere with the body's ability to shuttle nutrients into cells for tissue repair and energy production. As a consequence, physical deterioration at the cellular level, due to general wear and tear on the body, begins to outstrip the natural restoration process. Tissue degeneration, such as premature cartilage wear, can set in at an early age, accompanied by inflammation. Cardiovascular conditions can develop as the staging for diabetes progresses. Ultimately, carbohydrate or grain-filled feed causes the dog's body to age at a faster rate than it would if insulin were working at full potential.

THE IMPORTANCE OF DIETARY FAT

The **fat** component of a meal is important for your animal at all stages of its life, and this fat component includes both essential and non-essential fatty acids. Precious polyunsaturated fats are easily damaged during the manufacturing process and are most often missing from processed dog food. The main culprit in the destruction of fatty acids is oxidation—oxygen molecules do their work on fats quickly, causing that familiar rancid smell. In fact, because polyunsaturated fats are so susceptible to degradation, they are often removed from food so it can survive the long cycle of processing, storage, shipping, and more storage. The high heat used during common processing methods does enough damage to this important nutrient category to obliterate it completely.

Manufacturers of dry processed feeds may compensate for the damage done to these fats by adding polyunsaturated, essential, and non-essential Omega-6 and Omega-3 fatty acids back into their products to fortify them. We often see these additions on the label as ALA, EPA, DHA (Omega-3 fats), or linoleic acid (Omega-6 fat). This is a good marketing story, however, no matter what kind of preservatives they add to keep these fats intact, the long-term survival of the delicate structures is not possible. Studies done to show the value of these new fatty acid additives (DHA is one of the more common ones) are conducted using foods fresh off the manufacturing line. Shelf storage, oxygen-permeable bags, and open bags at home allow oxygen in, and it will degrade the fatty acids. And if the fortified fatty acid does make it to body cells intact, the other nutrients it requires in order to complete its cellular activity are also likely missing or in limited supply in the food. The cells' processing of essential and other fatty acids like DHA depends on a multitude of other, codependent nutrients, including vitamin and mineral cofactors. If these cofactors are not available, the cells cannot handle the fatty acids. Having the right balance and proportions of these codependent elements is critical.

Ensuring your dog gets nourishment that is nutrient dense, with good bioavailability and the right mix of nutrients can be a challenge. Many pet owners fall into a dog-food rut, convinced their pet is "picky" about its food. This can lead to undernourishment, particularly if the food is highly damaged during processing. Imagine eating the same dry, boxed cereal or canned item for every meal of your day. You know it's not possible to live a full life, free of disease if you're eating the same heavily processed food day after day. Yet most of us readily serve a steady diet of the same dry or canned processed food to our dogs without a second thought.

Just like you can't rely on boxed breakfast cereal to sustain good health, processed dog food alone will not maintain your dog's health. The manufacturers of these processed dog food products will tell you the food is fortified to meet all of your dog's nutritional needs, but so are our breakfast cereals, and we know that such nutrition is not good enough to sustain us for every meal of every day. Find a few different feeds, prepared in different ways, in order to present some variety. While other experts have advocated that feed should not be changed in order to maintain consistency, I strongly believe that variety is the key to properly nourishing your dog. And I have seen how proper nourishment with nutrient-dense, balanced meals full of bioavailable nutrients will support health and vigor that will be apparent in your pet's eyes, skin, coat, muscle tone, fatness, and even in the way they carry themselves.

ASSESSING PROCESSED PET FOODS

Heavily processed pet foods—dry kibble or the canned variety—often fail the quality test for more than one reason. First, they are not likely to be nutrient-dense. They usually contain those fillers we discussed in order to create bulk in the feed and give the food some texture. These fillers reduce the quantity of meat your pet is getting (and needs), while supplying nutrients (in the form of high-glyemic carbohydrate) that your pet does not need. Furthermore, once the fillers are digested, the chemical interaction of their elements with other nutrients hampers the delivery of the expected benefits of the quality ingredients. As you now know, these common fillers can also slowly degrade insulin efficiency.

The second reason processed pet foods fail the quality test is because the bioavailability of the nutrients in the quality ingredients is low. The processing of bagged and canned pet foods exposes the ingredients to air, moisture, light, and high levels of acid and heat for prolonged periods, and interaction with these elements alters the chemistry of the food. One of the key alterations happens when oxygen comes in contact with the food, changing the chemistry of the nutritional elements. This is a simplified description of the process of oxidation.

Where does oxidation happen? Opportunities for oxidation are created during the grinding and mincing processes, during exposure to extreme heat to kill microbes, and during storage and handling. Storage and handling of food leads to oxidation because once the manufacturer has assembled and tested the ingredients for a dried pet food, it can take many weeks for the product to be made and bagged. Those bags of finished food may sit in the manufacturer's warehouse for several more weeks before they are shipped to a distributor. There, they can sit for four or five weeks before reaching a retailer's shelves, to sit again at the retailer's, and again at your home, where the food bag may be opened and then not tightly resealed. All of this time and all of these steps provide opportunities for oxygen to interact with the food and rob it of most of the active nutrients it may have had.

As a result of the intense processing required to make a shelf-stable product like kibble, vitamins will be compromised structurally, minerals will bind together into indigestible forms, amino acids will bind into non-useable forms, and the quality of other nutrients, such as fats, will be degraded. The bioavailability of nutrients at the digestive level and the biological activity they offer the cells of the body will have been severely reduced.

The degree of heat and the duration it is applied during the preparation of dry commercial feeds determines the degree of nutrient degradation. The longer the heat is applied, the more the damage. Even if the nutrients are added back into the food to fortify it later, there is no guarantee they will still be available when the food hits your dog's bowl. Later exposure to air and light during long shelf storage (and home storage in less-than-ideal conditions) will damage the fortifying nutrients.

And aside from the shortcomings of a range of commercial pet foods due to processing, another reason highly processed commercial foods are less than ideal has recently come to light—the risk of contamination. Although serious cases of poisoning that have resulted in deaths and global recalls are fairly rare, milder contamination will go unnoticed and compromise health at a lower level. What was the cause the last time your dog seemed a bit lethargic or moody? Its body can absorb and detoxify some poisons, but later health consequences may develop without an obvious reason.

The melamine fiasco in 2007, which resulted in multiple pet deaths, was not about accidental poisoning of the food. It was caused when manufacturers of core ingredients—the raw materials—sought to improve profits by adding melamine to raise nitrogen levels of a processed feed. The addition gave the food or ingredient the appearance of higher protein content when it was tested to guarantee the level of protein in the feed. Unfortunately, not only is this artificial nitrogen or protein (melamine) source unavailable to the body for tissue repair, it is poisonous. This unthinkable scandal is something to seriously consider when choosing a pet food and contemplating the addition of protective supplementation to feeds. Monitoring for these contaminants is a very difficult task even for reputable brands since the supply chain for ingredients is long.

Agricultural feeds have been augmented by feed companies in similar ways for some time, but our domesticated cattle, chickens, and other food-sourced livestock don't live long enough for the consequences of these poisons to manifest. Companion animals live for a much longer time. If you ask any veterinarian, they'll tell you that kidney and liver diseases of no known cause have been significantly on the rise in dogs and cats in the last decade.

Again, the veterinary professional's common remedy for kidney disease is to move to protein-reduced feeds since the protein is implicated as the cause. Not only is the damaged protein building block contributing to more metabolic waste and subsequently more work by the kidneys and liver, but small, regular doses of these protein-associated poisons might be major factors in the organ failure.

In the case of wet, canned food, less oxidative damage may occur during processing, even though heat is applied when the can is prepared. However, once the can of pet food is opened, unless it is carefully sealed and kept in the refrigerator to preserve the leftovers, light and air will begin to degrade the contents. In addition, canned food often contains sugar and salts that are used as preservatives. The sugar additives in these foods raise your dog's insulin strain without adding any nutritional benefit.

The added salt brings its own set of complications. Household pets have a high incidence of urinary tract stones or infection. The most common stone is made up of calcium oxalate, caused by an imbalanced mineral intake, coupled with an unhealthy pH in the urine. A high-sodium diet triggers the release of calcium into the urine. If the pH conditions are acidic, this calcium precipitates out into painful crystal form. The crystals can be intrusive enough to contribute to infection. Interestingly, a diet high in that poor-quality protein that requires more intense metabolic processing contributes to the problem by changing the pH (acid-alkaline rating) of the urine. Processed foods tend to have sodium added to them while delivering damaged protein. This is the perfect recipe for urinary tract stones, especially for animals that have a genetic or metabolic predisposition for stone formation.

In addition to the problems with the ingredients, the cans themselves are often lined with plastic films that may leach compounds such as xenoestrogens (estrogen-mimicking chemicals) and other toxins associated with plastic into the food.

Freeze drying is another method used to produce commercial pet foods, and it is gaining popularity. While any form of processing that includes grinding the food and exposing the nutrients to light and oxygen for a period of time compromises the life-sustaining potential of the food, freeze-dried food is healthier than conventionally processed food produced with intense heat. The elimination of moisture helps preserve the nutrients, but freeze-dried feed will deteriorate during storage, which slowly eats away at the life of the delicate nutrients. Still, freeze-dried foods are a credible alternative to other, more heavily processed foods, and they are becoming more commonly available in retail shops that focus on healthier choices.

LOWER-QUALITY PET FOODS RESULT IN POORER PET HEALTH

I must stress that poor nutrition eventually results in the development of illness. This is a slow process that can be difficult to link to your dog's diet. Instead, you may think your pet's deterioration is part of the natural aging process. In fact, the average dog can maintain health and resist infection quite effectively if it is getting everything its body needs from a healthy diet and lifestyle. Aging will progress at a reasonably slow rate, and the vibrancy of youth can last for a long time.

Signs of compromised health include regular illness; symptoms of chronic diseases such as insulin resistance or diabetes (frequent urination, frequent and abundant water consumption, poor energy, sudden weight gain or weight loss); the chronic, uncontrolled inflammation associated with arthritis or tendonitis; ongoing problems with a pet's skin and coat; or recurring infections. The illness may not be anything specific, but you may notice that your companion animal seems to be "slowing down" or aging prematurely. Or your dog's immune system may not be able to protect it from pathogens that regularly infect or cause illness. Less obviously, chronic inflammation may be very mild (subclinical), resulting "only" in stiffness and mild discomfort, but it is doing damage nonetheless.

Illness and inflammation that stem from an unhealthy metabolism may lead you to depend on drugs such as immune suppressants, antibiotics, or anti-inflammatory drugs to manage your pet's recurring discomforts. Eventually, antibiotics may be required a few times a year to ward off pathogens that overcome your dog's weakened immune system. Instead, use nutritional tools, made available through your dog's diet, to empower a healthy immune system that can keep pathogens at bay.

A diet that is complete and includes less-processed foods will help your pet's body correct hormonal inefficiencies, while a diet of processed foods can contribute to an ongoing, negative hormonal influence. Processed and poorly regulated for toxicity, cardboard foods will speed your pet's aging.

Aging and AGES

Uncontrolled oxidation in the body combined with a high glycemic load courtesy of uncontrolled dietary carbohydrate can result in the development of compounds called AGES (advanced glycation end products). AGES are formed when sugars react with proteins in the body. And, yes, AGES accelerate the aging process. Secondary damage to the cardiovascular system, nerves, joints, and general inflammation associated with diabetes is also attributed to the effect of AGES. This damage begins in the pre-diabetes stage.

AGES can also form in the foods as they are processed if the carbohydrate and protein components are mixed in a moist environment while being exposed to high heat and air. This is exactly how dry and canned pet foods are made. The resulting AGES in the food are altered nutrients that cannot be used by the body to maintain or restore health, and a portion of these food-borne AGES can be absorbed to cause harm in the body. Interestingly, food-borne AGES are known to enhance flavor, and manufacturers often purposely incorporate them into processed foods to improve palatability.

A healthy diet, in the proper quantity and quality, boosts your dog's energy and immunity, slows the aging process, and reduces incidences of inflammation and insulin resistance. Knowing how difficult it is to maintain a healthy diet in a human family, the prospect of achieving this for your pet may seem daunting. While pets will rarely raid your cupboards or refrigerator if you keep food stored properly, they will snack on whatever is within reach. For the most part, however, whatever they eat is up to you. The nutrient density, bioavailability of nutrients, and ratio of protein, fat, and carbohydrate is under your control.

Dog food manufacturers work to balance quality and costs to create the best value they can for a price consumers are willing to pay. Consumers may resist a higher quality or quantity of nutrients in pet foods because of the higher cost, so manufacturers are not solely responsible for the compromised quality of pet foods. Pet foods that are nutrient-dense may be more expensive, but the recommended servings may be smaller, so they could still be better value. When you're reading the labels and comparing prices, compare the size of the recommended servings. Higher-quality foods are available in the marketplace if you look for them and if you use them as recommended, they may still fit your budget and lifestyle.

There is no question that dried and canned foods are convenient to use, however, weigh that convenience against the possibility of the growing health problems (and vet bills) that often result from inadequate nutrition. This possibility will become more likely as your dog ages. Younger dogs can tolerate nutrient insufficiency better than older dogs can for reasons that will be outlined in the pages to come. Your budget or your lifestyle may mean that you need to use these heavily processed pet foods some of the time, but don't make them your dog's only source of nourishment. Seriously consider adding dietary support in the form of multivitamin, multi-mineral, and antioxidant and phytoantioxidant supplements to counter the effects of processed foods.

Improvement in your dog's health and energy levels after adding a supplement to their meals can be immediate. This is because processed food can be so nutrient-damaged that slight changes in the dog's diet can make profound health improvements. Better nutrient availability can empower your dog's body to do its job, which is to restore and maintain health.

THE GOLD STANDARD: A RAW, WHOLE FOOD DIET

As you now know, a good diet for your pet supplies the right ratios of protein, fat, and carbohydrate in a nutrient-dense, bioavailable form. Raw foods can deliver the many benefits that food is intended to supply. The bodies of canines have evolved based on the nutrient profile of raw, natural (as opposed to synthetic) foods. This is no different from the way humans have developed. Research shows that our dogs depend on the nutritional elements that nature provides in the whole form.

A meal of appropriate fresh, whole, raw foods supplies live enzymes that bodies depend on for natural digestive and other processes. It also supplies live antioxidants that protect cells and tissues from damage and the body from illness. Raw, whole foods can best supply balanced nutrition that interacts with your dog's gene systems, and these foods are the healthiest way to nourish your dog. The right foods are nutrient-dense, and their nutrients are highly bioavailable after digestion because they haven't been damaged by processing. That said, feeding a dog a raw food diet is not about throwing Fido a slab of marbled T-bone steak.

Good protein sources include chicken, beef, and other muscle meats as the major source of protein. A raw food diet must also include cartilage-rich meats such as turkey or chicken necks in their whole, raw form. These can be purchased fresh or frozen for later use. For some pet owners, however, the thought of tossing the dog a whole turkey or chicken neck is too much to contemplate. Raw foods can be purchased in ground, blended, flash-frozen serving packages as a convenient alternative.

Despite the need for meat, be aware that organ meats should not be the major portion of the food. In particular, be wary of feeding too much liver meat. The liver is the detoxifying site of any animal's body. Modern prolific use of chemicals in agriculture and the environment exposes all living things to chemicals and toxins in many direct and indirect ways. These are dealt with by the liver and can become concentrated in the organs, particularly the liver, and other tissues of the animal used to make your dogs' food. Liver is a common flavoring and nourishing agent of foods, treats and supplements, but it should not be fed to your dog daily.

Fresh, whole foods contain the necessary fats, uncompromised by the need for long-term storage, and provide the other cofactor nutrients needed by the body to properly digest, absorb, and use the fat nutrients.

Dogs rely on small amounts of plant nutrients for the carbohydrate, enzyme, and fiber portions of their diet. The plant-based portion can also supply many vitamins, minerals, and even some important fatty acids if it is in its whole form. However dogs are highly sensitive to the type of plant sources used to supply these carbohydrate and other nutrients. Have you ever seen a wild wolf gnawing on a cob of corn or a sprinkle of rice or wheat? No. A good-quality raw food diet will provide sources of plant nutrients that do not cause the insulin spike that results when dogs eat grains. As noted earlier, the plant-based carbohydrate should come from low-glycemic vegetables and some fruits, such as yam, sweet potato, carrots, spinach, squash, apples, and pear. (Carrots are higher on the glycemic index but are acceptable.) Of course, wolves don't often chow down on vegetables and fruits either although they've been seen eating apples at the base of an apple tree, but these foods are lower on the glycemic index, and this means they do not have the same negative impact on blood sugar that corn, rice, and other grains will have. These preferred foods are also a rich source of antioxidants, vitamins, and minerals.

You might be wondering how dogs in the wild got access to plant nutrients before owners took over the role of foraging for food. In the wild, your dog's cousins eat the innards of their kill, including the stomach contents, which means they are consuming the vegetation that grazing prey has pre-digested for them.

Again, variety is important, even with a raw, whole food diet. Alternate the meat-and-vegetable combinations to supply a variety of nutrition from different sources. A reputable retailer will be able to provide you with properly prepared frozen raw foods, and by using some of the guidelines here you'll be able to make an educated choice.

Animals having perpetual health challenges often find reasonable relief within weeks of changing to a raw food diet. Although organic sources of meat and plant-based foods are the best choice for all of us, animals with fragile digestive systems might require the organic choice exclusively in order to end illness. Skin conditions, digestive impairments, and diarrhea can be eased or eliminated with a raw food diet. Some conditions may require the addition of nutritional supplements designed to treat the specific ailment in order to resolve the condition completely.

However, even raw foods cannot supply the nutrient density on their own that our pets may need to maximize health, vitality, and longevity. One reason is the nutrient profile of the meat itself. The nutritional profile of the meat derived from domesticated livestock is dependent on their feed. In other words, the man-made feeds for this meat source produce a man-made nutrient profile. Meat sources from animals in the wild will have a different nutrient profile that might include a higher mineral, vitamin, and even antioxidant levels. Domestic meat sources will also provide different fatty acid proportions that might not be as healthy as the fatty acid profiles found in wild meat sources.

Supplementation of a raw food diet with vitamin, mineral, and phytoantioxidants, as well as polyunsaturated fatty acid blends with linoleic acid and DHA, increases nutrient density and the health potential of raw feeds. And this increased health potential is not only required because of the nutrient limitations of the meat and plant sources used to make the food. The increasing oxidation and other forms of toxicity in our environment also contribute to an increased need for better nutrition (primarily antioxidant nutrition). Supplementation helps the body deal with this unnaturally elevated oxidative stress.

Keep in mind that illness is rarely caused by a genetic anomaly. A genetic factor that may be shared within the same gene-pool or bloodline—resulting in a condition that regularly occurs—might be related to the inability to tolerate processed food rather than a genetic predisposition to cartilage failure, for example. An animal with a better capacity to extract these nutrients from the diet has a lower risk of developing the same ailment. In other words, a reduced ability to extract key nutrients from food will result in the development of faulty tissues.

Even in cases of compromised digestive or nutrient absorption abilities, however, better-quality nourishment may empower the dog's body to restore health despite the digestive vulnerability. Improving the nutrient density of a dog's diet generally does improve these conditions by ensuring key nutrients are delivered to the cells. The nutritional therapies in these cases, again, are not miraculous medicines; they are merely essential tools needed for regular cellular maintenance. Raw foods are less likely to contain elements that interfere with digestion and metabolism, and they supply high-quality nutrients in easy-to-absorb and useful forms.

THE PREPARATION OF RAW, WHOLE FOODS

The challenge that comes with preparing a raw food diet is getting the proper combination of nutrients. The average dog thrives on meals that are 60 to 65 percent raw meat. The best way to deliver this is to use the entire carcass, including the organs and bones. The whole carcass will retain the most nourishment. Protein sources can include chicken—here the whole carcass is manageable—as well as beef, pork, lamb, and fish. Although the muscle meats supply the best quality protein, other protein sources such as connective tissues and organs provide a wider array of minerals and vitamins. Obviously, the best raw choices will be organic or free-range. These deliver a wide array of nutrition that has not been damaged by heat or chemicals, and it minimizes the potential for chemical contamination of your pet's food.

Your pet will surprise you as instincts kick in and the dog begins gnawing and then crunching right through the entire carcass—bones, cartilage, organs, and everything else in between. Raw bones can be included. Even chicken bones are not dangerous for carnivorous pets *if* they are raw. However, cooked bones can splinter and cause serious intestinal damage.

If your little carnivore's carcass crunch is too much to tolerate, freshly ground versions of raw meals are an alternative. The entire carcass, of a chicken for example, including the organs and bones can be ground into a coarse mince.

The vegetable component of the blend—35-40 percent—should be treated a little differently from the meat component. The vegetable component should not be ground as coarsely as the meat component. It should be finer to ensure that the nutrients are available to the animal's digestive process. Keep in mind that dogs do not have the digestive enzymes to break down plant foods (the plant cell walls), and, as a result, they are not able to easily extract vital nutrients within the plant cells. Each meal should feature some freshly crushed organic varieties of these vegetables.

A coarser grind protects the delicate cellular components of the food from oxidation and retains more nourishment, but your dog's digestive process may not be able to penetrate the coarse bits to extract enough of the nutrition. A fine grind breaks down more of the cells, exposing the delicate nutrients to the oxidative air and damage, but your dog relies on the finer grind to access the nutrients. The finer the grind, the more quickly the meal should be served after thawing or exposure to air. Keeping these facts in mind, you will have to be strategic about serving your pet these delicate nutrients. I purchase and serve a prepared combination of meats and vegetables to which I always add supplementation and often add extra pureed vegetables immediately after grinding them in a processor or blender.

If you are thinking of preparing raw food meals at home at least occasionally, some experts suggest that microbe risks such as salmonella and *E.coli* could be a concern. I don't believe this is a serious issue because dogs are not as vulnerable to these microbes as humans might be. These microbes do not survive in the dog's gastrointestinal tract as easily as they can in a human's intestinal tract.

The real risk with microbes is associated with the mishandling of raw food by the human feeders, which could result in illness in human family members. Keep infants and young children away from an animal immediately after it's had a raw food meal that may be contaminated with microbes, as well as keeping them away from the raw food itself and the preparation area. This risk is, in my opinion, overstated, but if you are considering a raw diet for your pet, be careful. Take the same precautions you would to prepare raw foods or meat for cooking for the rest of the family—wash your hands, food preparation surfaces, and utensils in hot water and antimicrobial cleaners when you're finished. You don't fear raw meat enough to keep it out of your human family members' diet. The preparation risk is not much different when it comes to raw food for your pet. Oil of oregano is a powerful antibacterial and antiviral agent; dilute solutions can be made to effectively disinfect preparation areas. You may also wish to use a separate set of utensils or area for the preparation of your pet's food. Use the same "Food Safe" strategies you would use when preparing your family's meals.

Keeping food and supplements within reach makes it easy to prepare your dog's meals each day. I dedicate a little cupboard to the canines. It houses their dry food kibble, used to top up their raw food. Yes, you read that correctly. I throw a sprinkling of a few kibble crunchies on their nutrient-rich raw food to provide some texture variation. It's not necessary, but I think they appreciate it. The canine cupboard also holds all of their supplements. Right next to the cupboard in the canine corner sits a small refrigerator where the thawed, fresh-frozen food waits. The frozen bulk food is in a small freezer in the garage. The refrigerator, freezer, small counter area, and little cupboard all belong to the dogs. This reduces the risk for cross-contamination and keeps everything organized and easily accessible.

WORKING WITH A RAW FOOD DIET

Changing to an alternative diet must be done carefully and gradually in order to prevent unnecessary stress for your dog. The transition should be done over a week or two as you gradually increase the proportion of raw food in the diet. If your dog just won't eat the higher-quality food you've chosen, what should you do? Make sure you stay in control, and do the same thing you would do to ensure your child is eating healthy meals. Most of our children would choose a bowl of ice cream over a nourishing dinner any day. Your dog will do the same. If the healthy dinner is not eaten, ice cream will not be available at the end of the meal. If your dog won't eat the healthier food choice immediately, just leave it out until your pet is hungry enough to eat it.

Eventually your dog will eat—and acquire a taste for the improved nutrition fast. Your dog won't starve even if he misses a few meals. And I can assure you he won't let himself starve no matter how fussy he might lead you to believe he is.

My two dogs are fed a diet that is primarily raw. Sometimes this raw food is organic; other times it is not. I am careful to use oil of oregano to wipe the working surfaces, the bowls, and my hands clean of microbes. Even though I use raw food, I still add supplements to maximize nutrient density. Most importantly, I add a fatty acid supplement to their feed—one that has been specifically formulated for the canine metabolism. I also add a very dense vitamin, mineral, phytoantioxidant powder. My dogs also get raw turkey or chicken necks two or three times a week.

Raw turkey or chicken necks are nature's perfect canine toothbrushes. As the dog's teeth sink into the fresh cartilage, calculus and bacteria are sloughed off. The gums are stimulated by this physical activity, promoting healthy blood flow. Commercially dried cookie-like treats do not have the same effect; neither do the dried kibble bits.

Raw Eggs

Should you give your dog raw eggs? Raw eggs can interfere with the absorption of biotin, which is an important vitamin that helps your dog's coat and skin and is involved in many cellular processes, including energy metabolism. A protein, namely avidin, in the egg white can bind to biotin in the gut, rendering it unavailable for absorption. Raw eggs also carry the risk of salmonella poisoning. This is not a huge threat, but it can compromise health.

On the plus side, raw eggs provide a great source of bioavailable protein and fats, and if poor-quality food is on the menu, an egg a week will enhance coat quality simply by supplying nutritional elements that kibble may not be able to provide. If kibble is fed as a main source of nutrition, a raw or flash-cooked egg should be added one meal each week. My dogs get a raw egg approximately one meal per week. As always, moderation is the key. If eggs are given more often—such as three times per week to supplement the meal's protein content, they must be cooked in order to deactivate the avidin.

True to the relationship between convenience and what's best nutritionally, preparing high-nutrient raw foods at home is quite a process. Most pet owners cannot commit to the regime because of the time required. Fortunately, there are some reliable brands in the marketplace that do a great job of preserving whole, raw foods in a pre-blended format. Just buy frozen, fresh-food blends prepared in the way described above. The nutrients in commercially prepared raw food should be much more biologically available and valuable than processed food, but, again, exposure to elements such as air and light trigger the oxidation of nutrients and some fatty acid degradation.

Commercially prepared, fresh raw food is usually frozen in serving-size packages that must be defrosted. The way the raw food is prepared and blended before it's frozen for commercial sale plays a role in how much of the naturally occurring nourishment is preserved. Regardless of the preparation methods, the nutrients are best if the food is defrosted as required and served almost immediately.

Today many different brands of raw food are available in the stores. I have also found that butchers who have sold meats for human customers their entire careers are starting to produce their own versions of raw pet foods that are made with human-grade ingredients. I rely on my new pet-serving butcher to grind and blend chicken thighs (bone in) with a vegetable mix made up of yams, spinach, peas, and broccoli. The chicken thighs may make up 65 percent of the recipe by weight while the vegetable component in total will make up about 35 percent of the recipe's total weight. The whole carcass is also acceptable but may have a lower protein content in the end than the chicken thighs as the exclusive meat source. As long as the blend is based on sound scientific principles, this is my preferred choice since the ingredients are primarily human-grade. Creating biologically appropriate foods for our pets is not as simple as blending a multi-ingredient *minestrone*. These recipes may be best left to experienced professionals to concoct.

HOW MUCH IS ENOUGH?

The amount of food that is appropriate on a daily basis depends on your dog's size, age, and level of activity. Whether you're using frozen raw blends or other commercially prepared products, feeding tables will be supplied by the manufacturers. Check the label on the food of choice and start with the recommended amounts for your pet's circumstances. However, don't use the feeding chart by weight on the label as an absolute instruction. Use the recommendation as a starting point and monitor your pet's weight. If you notice a weight gain, don't hesitate to cut back on the quantity. Excess weight puts stress on your pet's organs and joints and can lead to insulin resistance and inflammation. Your dog is unlikely to turn down a meal or a treat, so it's up to you to control the quantities. The key is to be aware of your pet's activity status on a day-to-day or weekly basis. If you've had an active day with your companion canine, you'll know that day to increase the feed volume slightly as compensation for the greater demand.

The nutrient density of the chosen food will affect the quantity your dog needs. A food that has fillers in place of quality protein, essential fat, or suitable carbohydrate sources will leave your dog undernourished and wanting more. However, a high quantity of lower-density nutrition can result in too many calories. Instead, choose a higher-*quality* food that provides a higher level of vitamins and minerals and meets essential fatty acid requirements. This food can likely be given in smaller quantities. As an alternative, the nutrient density of a borderline meal can be increased without bumping up the calories significantly by adding quality vitamin, mineral, and fatty acid supplements. Raising the nutrient density of the meal in this way improves your dog's antioxidant status and its immune system potential.

Pet owners often associate food with love or positive reward. Even if your food and treats are made of quality nutrition, too much of a good thing still leads to weight gain. If this is your preferred way of signaling approval, then you'll likely reward good behavior with food. Don't reward your dog to death by over-feeding for good behavior. And if you're not able to spend time with your dog one day or one week, don't hand out more treats as a sign of your love. Given modern, busy schedules, the result of this reward system could be an obese dog with a higher risk for diabetes, heart problems, lethargy, and joint disorders. Food is not love—not for humans or dogs.

Instead, reward your dog with a favorite toy. Rotate popular toys so your pet doesn't get bored with them. Better yet, reward your pet by playing their favorite game or heading out together for a walk in the park.

When you do offer a food treat, be aware that the dried treats you choose for your pet as a reward are just as damaged nutritionally as other pet foods unless you carefully select versions that are naturally preserved. I like to use dehydrated chicken strips—real chicken muscle meat dried to a crisp—as an occasional treat.

FREE-FEEDING OR A TIGHT SCHEDULE?

Generally, it is best if your dog consumes smaller, more frequent meals each day instead of a single, large meal that may overwhelm the digestive process and intestinal absorption sites. Two smaller meals a day, in the morning and early evening, are preferable. I feed my two dogs immediately after I eat my breakfast, and immediately after I eat my dinner.

Free-feeding is an alternative that might seem to be a practical solution if your lifestyle makes a feeding schedule impossible. With free-feeding, the food bowl is topped up, and the dog determines how much and when to eat. If you consider the way the wild cousins of dogs feed, free-feeding is an invitation to obesity. All mammals—dogs and humans—have ancestors who gorged when food was available and fasted when it was not. Wild dogs and wolves bring down their animal prey in a feeding frenzy. However, the abundance resulting from killing a large animal is usually followed by a period of scarcity that includes only the odd small prey, like a rabbit or a rodent. Ultimately, the way these wild animals feed is a "feast or famine" system.

Animals in the care of a responsible owner are not going to see a famine, although some experts believe that it doesn't hurt to skip a feeding day in order to mimic what your pet's wild cousins may experience. Even though I occasionally skip a meal, I will not skip a day of feeding.

The choice of feed will dictate the feeding schedule to a certain extent. Raw food, either the fresh, frozen variety or the home-prepared version, must be consumed as soon as it's been prepared or thawed if the nutrients are to have the best effect. It cannot sit in a bowl and deteriorate until the dog decides to eat, and thus it's not conducive to a free-feeding schedule.

What's in a bowl?

Use hygienic bowls, such as ceramic or high-quality stainless steel, for food. Plastics can be porous and harbor microbes, and they can contribute toxic xenoestrogens and other contaminants common to plastics to the meal. (Xenoestrogens are compounds that mimic natural estrogens in the body and disrupt hormonal cascades and balances. They can also contribute to the development of obesity and cancer.)

Ensure food bowls are stable, with rubber grip pads on the bottom. Although each bowl should be sanitized after feeding, I have to admit I don't do it regularly. My dogs do a great job of thoroughly polishing their bowls, but this doesn't mean the bowls are microbe-free.

If infants and young children have access to food bowls, the bowls must be removed from the floor and cleaned after each meal, especially if it's a raw food meal. It wouldn't hurt to also wipe them using a dash of oil of oregano as a natural disinfectant.

Since I feed outside, I usually leave the bowls out until the next feed and only sanitize them about twice a week. If these bowls remained inside, where my children, including one infant, would have close contact, I would sanitize them after each feeding and put them away.

Water bowls should be made of the same materials. I sanitize the stainless steel water bowls once a week but rinse them thoroughly at least three times a week. Toxic disinfectant chemicals are not necessary for sanitation; oil of oregano works very well.

NOURISHING DOGS AT DIFFERENT LIFE STAGES

Manufacturers of commercial dog foods have done a great job of marketing the value of life-stage or age-specific food blends. However, as much as a puppy's or senior animal's nutritional needs differ from those of an adult dog, there are also many similarities. I find that the best way to address the differences is with stage-specific supplements that provide the age-related nutrients in functional doses and in forms the body can easily absorb and use given its state of maturity (or lack of).

The alternative is to have these important nutrients blended into the feed when it is manufactured and this is, in fact, the most convenient. However, once these specialized ingredients are mixed into a processed feed, their availability to the digestive process is subject to the same degradations outlined earlier. Supplementing the feed with fresh nutrients at each meal ensures those nutrients are active and free of digestive encumbrances. For complete information on how the supplements work with the dog food of your choice, see Chapter 3: From Good Nutrition to Biologic Nutrition.

KEEPING YOUR PET HYDRATED: THE IMPORTANCE OF WATER

Although a healthy animal might survive weeks without food, it usually cannot survive for more than a few hot days without an abundant supply of clean water. We tend to forget the value of water because it's readily available everywhere we turn. However, the availability, freshness, and cleanliness of the water our pets drink is something we should be aware of.

Since our dogs tend to have a higher tolerance for microbes than we have, their immune systems can protect them from the contaminants found in standing water sources such as puddles. However, they are just as vulnerable to common pollutants in their water as we are, and their faster metabolisms mean that family pets can be affected more quickly by contaminated water than members of their human family will be. Thus the same exposure to contaminants in a shared water supply may cause your pet to develop disease sooner than the humans in the family might. Heed the warnings your pet offers. As much as I hate to think of it this way, these little guys are truly our coalmine canaries, and water-based illness and recovery from illness in them could shed some light on preventing illness in the human members of the family.

If pets have reliable sources of water available, they will be less likely to drink from puddles, ditches, and other sources of standing water they come across. It is quite possible that these sources could be contaminated by herbicide, pesticide, or fertilizer runoff or harmful microbes that breed in standing water.

Pesticides, heavy metals, and harmful microbes can leach into public water supplies. Although our North American water treatment programs are reasonably efficient, we are still vulnerable to toxins such as heavy metals. Chlorination of the water supply reduces the risks associated with pathogens, but researchers are showing today that the byproducts of chlorination might be responsible for the higher rates of tumors in the brain, kidney, and liver. And fluoride has been linked to skin disease, and in some reports, even cancer, to provide controversy for fluoridation programs. As much as fluoride supplementation can improve tooth and bone development, too much fluoride can make teeth and bones brittle and vulnerable to disease. Choose the water supplies for you and your family members carefully.

If you feed primarily with dry food, the availability of adequate water becomes even more important. Dogs eating dry kibble need to drink more water than those eating foods—such as raw foods—that contain water. Although a source of distilled water offers the cleanest source of water for pets, some researchers are concerned about the lack of minerals in distilled water. For this reason, my dogs get tap water on some bowl refills and a filtered source in the remaining refills, which is sometimes a distilled version and other times a bottled water supply derived from reverse osmosis.

Regardless of the water choices you make, reliable, continuous access to clean sources of water is critical to overall pet health. My three dogs have access to four water bowls in the backyard while we are away for the day. These bowls are spread throughout the area but always left in the same places so they know where to find them. I will include more than four bowls on extremely hot days. The distribution is a precautionary measure to ensure they have a backup supply in case one is turned over by accident. If the bowls were close together, a spontaneous play fight might empty all of them at once. These strategies are important in the hot summer months, when water must be available at all times. However, in the cold winter months when it's possible that the water will freeze, you have to be able to offer alternate sources of fresh water if pets spend their entire day outside. Electric bowls that are self-heating are available.

Water bowls must be monitored, and water should be changed daily. You may want to assign responsibility for a pet's water supply to a member of the family who doesn't share the feeding responsibilities in order to ensure that this priority is met. And make sure that your "water monitor" tells you if your dog has stopped drinking water.

Research shows that a vulnerability to pro-inflammatory states can be partly attributed to dehydration. Keep in mind that most illnesses are characterized by underlying inflammation, and this is why most diseases are treated with different types of anti-inflammatory drugs.

The research on water deficiency does not mean that water is a cure for most illnesses, but hydration is definitely important when it comes to maintaining general health and promoting recovery from disease.

THREE

FROM GOOD NUTRITION TO BIOLOGIC NUTRITION

The best feed you can offer the family dog is raw, fresh, whole food in the proper ratio of protein, fat, and carbohydrate. For many owners, this way of feeding is only possible as an occasional treat or not possible at all. The next best thing is the highest-quality freeze-dried food. If this will not work for you, then oven-dried (moderate heat), preservative-free, processed kibble is a reasonable and convenient option. More conventionally prepared kibble or canned foods are at the bottom of the list of quality choices.

Each of the feed choices available can be substantially improved by the addition of a base of vitamin, mineral, fatty acid, antioxidant, and active enzyme supplementation to bring the nutrient density, bioavailability of nutrients, and ratio of protein, fat, and carbohydrate to the optimum level. Not only is the nutrient density improved with this supplementation, the digestion and absorption of the feed's nutrients can be improved by the supplement. And you should increase the nutrient supplement dosing according to the level of processing of your chosen feed. It's a simple fact that as more steps are involved in the processing of the feed, and particularly as more intense heat is applied, higher levels of supplementation are required to restore the nutritional quality of what's going into your dog's food bowl.

Supplementation is the best pet health insurance you can buy (and the least expensive). A healthy, vigorous dog has a better quality of life and is a happy addition to your family, as contrasted with one that is unwell and in need of frequent trips to the vet.

If you choose feeds carefully and supplement strategically, your dog will be able to overcome common health challenges such as skin conditions, digestive difficulties, diarrhea, and the pain and destruction associated with inflammation. It should also be able to fight off the effects of mild contamination by low-level toxicity in substances it has consumed.

Another reason to supplement is because the dietary needs of one animal can be so different from another's that one blanket nutrient density supplied by a bagged feed may not suffice for an animal needing that extra boost. Meeting the demand of that more nutritionally needy pet by supplementing ensures that no diet-based limitations occur, and it serves as powerful health insurance.

KEY SUPPLEMENTS FOR OPTIMAL HEALTH

A good pet food supplement is needed to supply the basic vitamins and minerals that are often destroyed during food processing, preparation, and storage. (You and your human family members may take a daily multi-vitamin and mineral supplement for the same reason.) Beyond vitamins and minerals to equip the cells with essential cofactors and building blocks, fuel the body, and boost the immune system, what else does your pet's food need? You should be adding enzymes for digestion and fatty acids and antioxidants to complete your dog's nutrition.

Fatty acid supplementation is crucial in this day and age because the polyunsaturated fatty acids that are essential for life are extremely vulnerable to oxidation. These delicate fatty acid nutrients are among the first to be damaged by processing and environmental oxidants that are abundant today. Supplementing them in their undamaged active form and in the ratios your dog's metabolism requires empowers the body to resist illness and premature wear and tear.

A comprehensive supply of active enzymes aids the digestion of the protein found in processed dog food. Heat treatment during processing damages the chemical structure of protein, making it difficult for the dog's body to use it. Heat can also create protein complexes that actually damage organs. Supplementing with a broad spectrum of active digestive enzymes improves the digestibility of all the nutrients in the food being served. This increases feed efficiency (food value) and biological value, and it can even help reduce excrement volume since more nourishment is being absorbed from each mouthful.

The addition of enzymes is necessary even if you are feeding your dog raw, whole foods. This supplementation will also help deal with that small amount of the right, nutrient-dense vegetables required for canine health despite the fact that dogs cannot digest plant-based foods very well. Your dog's lack of digestive enzymes to break down the walls of plant cells means that supplementation can provide tremendous health benefits even in the case of a raw food diet. Although fine grinding and juicing these plant food sources to break down the plant cell walls will help release many of the valuable nutrients, it won't completely compensate for the lack of enzymes needed to digest them. You can improve digestion and absorption of even raw foods by supplementing the enzymes needed to digest and extract the appropriate plant nutrients. When you are choosing feed that is not raw, many of the plant nutrients must themselves be supplemented.

In the case of polyunsaturated, essential, and non-essential fatty acids, supplementation of the delicate molecules at feeding time can restore those nutrients and help reduce the inflammation that leads to painful conditions such as arthritis. Supplementation, especially in the case of fatty acid supplements, must be species-specific. This is critically important. Too many fatty acid supplements in the marketplace were designed for humans and simply relabeled. Dogs have a very different essential fatty acid requirement than you and me, and they need a very different fatty acid profile in their fat supplement. This means the ratio between Omega-3 alpha linolenic acid and Omega-6 linoleic acid, as well as the requirement of Omega-3 DHA and EPA is different for our dogs. Our human supplements don't provide our pets with the long-term benefits we'd expect. Neither do the salmon or other cold-water fish oils often added to dog food as fatty acid sources on their own. These required marine fats should not be supplied on their own because they are highly reactive and vulnerable to oxidation.

Fatty acids must be supplemented in the context of properly combined antioxidants that protect the active state of the fats and guide them down the right biochemical pathways in the cells. I refer to this as active or guided supplementation, as opposed to the common practice of passive supplementation that often fails.

While the fatty acid supplements must be in the proper proportion to promote cellular health, the accompanying antioxidants must themselves be precisely chosen and measured, targeting the right gene systems and neutralizing specific free radicals that might interfere with the work of the fatty acids and gene activity.

Antioxidants form a protective shield that neutralizes free radicals that would otherwise steal electrons from fatty acids and other precious molecules and promote inflammation. Research shows that many common ailments, including diseases as vicious as cancer, can be linked at least in part to a lack of dietary antioxidants. Good antioxidant nutrition does not just play a critical role in optimal health and quality of life; it also creates the foundation for emotional and cognitive health. A poorly nourished pet will display emotional instability and sub-par learning capacity.

SUPPLEMENTATION IS ESSENTIAL TODAY

Supplementation is essential today because the state of the food supply is compromised. Fruits and vegetables are picked earlier in their maturation phase and ripen during transit. This reduces the initial nutrient density of plant sources of food. These are the same plant sources used for production of dog foods—both raw and processed. They are the food sources we eat as well. In addition, domesticated animals such as chickens and cattle are nourished using man-made feeds. These man-made feeds for animal sources of food produce man-made nutritional profiles in the meat, bones, fat, and other tissues that are different than the nutritional profiles nature would produce.

Bone meal has become a common addition to pet foods as a supplement as well as an ingredient in the food itself to fortify the manufactured food. The objective is to provide a healthy supply of bone-supportive minerals like calcium, magnesium, copper, zinc, and others. However, has anyone ever thought about the nutritional state of the bone meal itself? Bone meal is simply the finely ground bone of the animals like cattle that we use as food sources. We rarely hear about compromised bone mass in cattle, but these cows don't live long enough for the physical consequences of these deficiencies to manifest at epidemic levels. The status of their bone minerals is ultimately a function of the nutrition in the man-made feed they eat and may not be the best source for your precious companion animal.

The bone mass can also carry toxins such as excessive fluoride deposits. Research is showing that this source of bone minerals as supplementation or as a food fortification ingredient may not be sufficient for our pets and can even be a source of toxicity if used abundantly. The alteration in the nutritional benefit of the meat and fat tissues is also evident when we compare our typical farmed fish to wild fish meat and oils. Fish oils of farmed fish can have a very different profile from the oils derived from wild cold-water fish. The same differences are apparent when comparing wild meat to comparable meat of our domesticated cattle and birds. Supplementation with the correct proportion of Omega-3 to Omega-6 fatty acids can correct this food-borne problem to ultimately restore order within your dog's body. A proper mineral supplement that guarantees the mineral quantities can also support good health. The result is better health management and improved tolerance to illness.

Another reason supplementation is required is the ever-escalating assault of the environment on our antioxidant stores. A stressful lifestyle that may include anxiety can also contribute to oxidation in the body and further deplete antioxidant levels. The unnaturally higher level of oxidation calls for a higher level of nutrient-based antioxidants as compensation. This additional support becomes even more important for our seniors as our dog's natural antioxidant production within its cells begins to decline. Supplementation is powerful health insurance.

THE BiologicVET PROGRAMS FOR OPTIMAL NUTRITION AND HEALTH

BiologicVET nutrient-based programs have been designed specifically to supplement everyday pet nutrition as well as treat a few specific conditions. The formulations are based on a decade of research in the lab and twenty years of personal experience in the field of both veterinary and human health care.

BiologicVET started out as a service to treat and save animals challenged by chronic illness that drugs and conventional allopathic strategies could not treat effectively. Drugs typically treat the symptom of disease. Luckily for us and our pets, many pharmaceutical protocols are able to do so with great efficiency, but often this relief comes with a side-effect, especially if the drugs are required long term. Recovery from the ailment requires metabolic correction and not just relief of symptoms. BiologicVET formulations are designed to deliver metabolic correction.

Over the years of treating animals, it became clear that many of the difficult cases were similar even though they are presented as different ailments. The discomfort and pain was caused or made worse by metabolic problems common to many different illnesses. In essence the required treatment strategy involved a broader approach to treat these common metabolic problems and a more focused approach to target the specific condition at the same time.

The first element of the BologicVET formulations is a broader vitamin and mineral treatment that empowers immune system health and function, gastrointestinal efficiency, nutrient transport, and general antioxidant saturation. Each therapeutic powder incorporates this general support to improve metabolic efficiency so that the powerful nutragenomic strategy—the second element of each formulation (which is also built into the condition-specific therapeutic products)— can do its job without the interference of a substandard metabolism. The formulation design uses a holistic approach. This second element of each condition-specific formulation precisely targets genes responsible for restoration of the tissues and metabolic systems at the root of the illness. The two-pronged approach is powerful, but, most importantly, it creates self-sufficient health and long-term recovery as opposed to relief of symptoms and recurring illness.

Many of the common illnesses also involve uncontrolled immune system activity that attacks the tissues of the body—autoimmune disease. As much as these conditions can be profound assaults on the system with few alternatives to immune-suppressing drugs, these few natural alternatives can be just as powerful as the drugs without the common side-effects that include cancers and vulnerability to pathogens and other opportunists. These autoimmune diseases include rheumatoid arthritis, lupus, Crohn's disease, and colitis, to name just a few of the common ones. BiologicVET remedies use these natural technologies.

Interestingly, many illnesses that may not be categorized as autoimmune conditions but involve uncontrollable, intense inflammation are also a function of an over-active immune system. These can be mitigated effectively with the administration of precisely engineered herbal extracts that modify and restore immune system health and accuracy. The same is achievable for the human members of the family with these conditions using human-intended strategies.

The BiologicVET products are specifically designed for the canines and felines in the family; they boost nutrient density, improve bioavailability with proper digestive enzymes, and supply missing fatty acids, antioxidants, vitamins, minerals, and other enzymes. This strategy provides a bounty of health-promoting nutrients in a form that is easy to digest and absorb. It also improves your dog's ability to extract and use nutrients in the food you have chosen. The heightened nutrient density aids in recovery from disease and helps your dog's body withstand the deterioration that comes with aging.

The formulations are not just one or two ingredients. Instead, they are comprehensive and complex. This approach is needed when maintaining health or treating illness because, although a single or perhaps just a few of the multiple ingredients deliver the necessary results, without the proper support from other nutrients the cells rely on, the key ingredients cannot fulfill their function. These formulations of multiple ingredients stimulate multiple biological activities at the same time, so multiple biological systems are working together for the same biological goal. Maintenance of health is not possible unless all biological systems are working at full capacity at all levels, including the cellular level.

For example, if a formula is targeting recovery of the joints, it must support immune system function to ensure it is not over-reacting and gastrointestinal tract efficiency so the nutrients can reach their target sites from oral doses. Each of these systems requires multiple ingredients for treatment as well. The formula must also maximize antioxidant levels in the body to neutralize oxidation and the ensuing inflammation that blankets in the body in the case of illness, making way for the healing nutrients, and this too involves multiple ingredients. How else could the required tissue-specific or gene-specific nutrients and cofactors make it from food to target site, such as the cartilage, if the gastrointestinal tract and the cells along the way are not supported?

In fact, an animal challenged by illness often experiences associated stress that can compromise gastrointestinal efficiency and produce oxidation in the body beyond the oxidation triggered by the illness. In turn, this can reduce nutrient absorption and activity in the body to compound the problem further. The formula must accommodate these needs in the treatment of the joint condition that might first appear to be far removed from these other supportive systems. Recovery from illness requires a multi-nutrient, multi-level approach.

This presentation of nutrients in multi-ingredient formulations is the key to the effectiveness of the BiologicVET program: one group of nutrients may support digestion of a gene-active nutrient; another group will assist in transporting a key nutrient to cells; another might be needed to keep a key nutrient from binding to another and becoming useless during digestion or transport; another nutrient or group of nutrients may be needed to support cell and even nuclear pore permeability; others may be required to defuse free radicals (oxidation) on the path of the key nutrient.

Beyond the need for a variety of ingredients, each ingredient must be delivered in doses that will be effective. Only research-supported doses allow each ingredient to follow through on its role. And finally, the format of the supplement has a big influence on its effectiveness. The powder format is best since it would not be possible to stuff a tablet or capsule with all of these ingredients at functional doses. Such a serving size could include ten to twenty tablets, and this would not be functional.

Newer nutrition-based strategies and therapies take this complexity into account and rely on the emerging research in nutrigenomics, which is the science of nutrients interacting with genetic signaling. My work developing the Biologicvet program of nutrition-based therapies was based on working with the cells' capacity to interpret and act on genetic instructions and hormonal signals. It also takes into account how the diet and other lifestyle factors influence genes through oxidation, glycemic index, AGEs, food processing, and more.

Biologicvet's comprehensive nutrient combinations provide both the tools and the context for successful nutrition-based therapy. There are two supplementation programs. The disease-prevention foundation is made up of BioFATS and BioVITES. We call this the Nutritional Foundation. These products give general metabolic support in the form of fatty acids, antioxidants, vitamins, and minerals. There are also three condition-specific therapies: BioJOINT, BioSKIN&COAT, and BioSLIM, along with BioSPORT performance enhancement for active dogs and BioSENIOR for aging pets. These seven, easy-to-use products can be delivered in any combination. Just add the powder or liquid to the pet food of your choice for a supply of the active vitamins, minerals, fats, and antioxidants that are often destroyed during food processing.

The key word is "active." Supplementation with Biologicᴠᴇᴛ products puts the life force back into the food. The Biologicᴠᴇᴛ products are made under very strict conditions to avoid contact with moisture and heat and limit oxidation to a minimum. The type of nutrients chosen for the formulations exhibit utmost stability, digestibility, and bioavailability so your pet is able to easily digest and absorb the rich benefits.

If you use regular pet food, adding Bɪoꜰᴀᴛs and Bɪoᴠɪᴛᴇs to your pet's food will help block the higher glycemic load created by grains and sugars used as fillers and flavoring in popular pet foods. Your dog will be less likely to develop insulin resistance. The Biologicᴠᴇᴛ foundation program also neutralizes the effect of free radicals. This antioxidant action is the key to the success of both programs. The supplements compensate for the effects of oxidation of food (as well as oxidation happening inside the body) and protect the nutrients all the way to the cells. That is why daily supplementation is such powerful protection against disease and premature aging.

The supplements in the Biologicᴠᴇᴛ program are delivered in powders and liquids that can be mixed with your pet's food because these forms work better for animals than tablets or chewable supplements. Tablet and capsule binders and other ingredients that are commonly used in the manufacture of pills can block the absorption of nutrients. Your dog's dietary nutrients travel down a shorter intestinal tract in the digestive system at a faster rate than your own so it's best to eliminate as much interference as possible to improve bioavailability of the supplements. And, as anyone who has ever tried to give a pill to a dog can attest, tablets and capsules are hard to administer. It's even harder to ensure that they have actually been swallowed.

BioFATS

BioFATS is a highly researched ratio of omega-3 and omega-6 fatty acids designed specifically for your dog. The ratio of these polyunsaturated fatty acids needed for optimal canine health is different from that needed for optimal human health and different again than a ratio that other species like your cat might need.

Within days of using BioFATS your dog's skin health can improve noticeably to alleviate dry flakey and even irritated, itchy conditions. Coat luster, color and excessive shedding can be improved using BioFATS. General demeanor including better mobility and mental health (behavior) can often improve using the highly specialized BioFATS formulation.

These more visible improvements in health when the supplement is administered are merely a function of the cells getting the 'essential fat' nutrition they need to maintain health spontaneously. The less than healthy state of skin and coat and even dysfunctional behavior issues can often be caused by deeper metabolic impairment that a fatty acid-limited diet can cause. Allowing this deeper insufficiency to continue will eventually lead to more illnesses.

Fatty acid deficiency is more common than we'd expect because bagged and canned food supply is so intensely processed that these highly reactive polyunsaturated fatty acids cannot survive the heat and long-term shelf storage.

Not only does the processing damage these essential fatty acids; our food sources, themselves, are usually deficient due to common agricultural practices that limit fatty acid balance in the meat and vegetation. Supplementation with properly proportioned essential fatty acid nutrition is essential today.

BioFATS includes the careful and precise addition of both essential and non-essential (sometimes called conditionally essential) fatty acids that are a key part of any health-affirming, disease prevention program. 'Conditionally essential fatty acids' are those that are technically categorized as non-essential. Your dog's body should be able to manufacture these non-essential fatty acids to meet demands. However, the tired cells of a senior dog may not be able to produce them in high enough quantities. A sick animal may not be able to produce enough of these fats in their cells to meet demand either. In these cases, a non-essential fatty acid is known to be conditionally essential. In the face of this condition, the nonessential fatty acid is now required essentially from the diet in order for health to prevail.

BioFATS is a fast-acting formula that can help to prevent the onset of disease, as well as help treat chronic illnesses and reduce inflammation. It fills the need for essential and conditionally essential fatty acids making certain that the body does not fall short of supply regardless of the circumstances. BioFATS is one of the two Nutritional Foundation products.

KEY INGREDIENTS

Dogs need linoleic acid, the Omega-6 fat, in their diet or supplement each day, and if it is not limited in the diet, a healthy dog should be able to manufacture all of the other fats it needs, including Omega-3 fats. (This Omega-6 fat is the only truly essential fatty acid as far as dogs are concerned.)

However, illness and age are not the only factors that can result in this essential fatty acid to be misused. A limitation in vitamins, minerals and antioxidants that the body needs to convert the essential fat into important Omega-3 and other non-essential fats will also create limitations in the body. And this results in Omega-3 fats like ALA, DHA and EPA (which the body should be manufacturing) being required in higher levels from the diet to compensate for the lack of production in the body- it makes these Omega-3 fats conditionally essential.

Most of us rely on processed bagged and canned foods as a nourishment staple for our pets. Not only is much of our food and that of our pets' this day and age, lower in nutrient density than fresher organically grown sources, processing also damages these delicate fatty acids and the nutrients the cells need to use them properly in the body. Bagged and canned foods are convenient but the goodness that is listed on the label cannot survive the process and time on the shelf.

Since it is hard to know if your animal is getting enough of all the nutrients it needs, including all the essential and non-essential fatty acids it needs, it's best to simply supplement with the proper ratio of the essential Omega-6 fatty acid and the health-promoting Omega-3 fatty acids (ALA, DHA, and EPA). BioFATS delivers all of them.

In addition to having the right amount of the right kind of fats, BioFATS also supplies the right *proportion* (or ratio) of fats. Not only is it important that the right Omega-6 to Omega-3 ratio be supplied, but it is just as important that the ratio between the Omega-3s EPA and DHA be precise for the intended biological effect in the cells. Salmon oil is combined with other marine oils to establish the correct Omega-3 balance of DHA and EPA and then combined with plant seed oils in the right combinations to meet the specific ratios of Omega-3 to Omega-6 fatty acids that dogs need. Salmon oil alone does not supply right amounts of the Omega-6 essential fatty acid, linoleic acid. BioFATS supplies the full complement of fats in the correct ratios in an easy-to-use liquid format.

Key vitamins, minerals and other nutrients such as fatty acids depend on many other nutrients to deliver their activity. If one is missing or limited, health and vitality are also limited. The Nutritional Foundation made up of BioFATS and BioVITES is designed to fulfill this comprehensive, codependent need. Even when it comes to the production of non-essential nutrients, if one small element is missing the cells cannot manufacture their needs. This is often the cause of the DHA and EPA limitations in the cells, and the reason skin conditions and immune system health are often compromised.

Conventional Fat Supplements
The cold-water fish oils from salmon, tuna, sardine, or mackerel that are often used as fat supplements don't supply sufficient levels of linoleic acid (Omega-6 fat), but they do provide Omega-3 fats such as DHA and EPA to deliver the building blocks for healthy cell membrane structure, positive receptor site status, and good hormone balance. Nevertheless, the impact of this selective fatty acid supplementation is limited because it is incomplete.

The key to establishing balance in the cells is balanced supplementation, and this means live linoleic acid must be available to do its job with the cold-water-fish-derived EPA and DHA. Although the Omega-6 linoleic acid is thought to be abundant (and more stable than the Omega-3 fatty acids) in our meat sources, it too can be damaged by intense food processing and become deficient in the diet.

The benefits of BioFATS will be obvious in three to five days. Your dog's skin will be healthy, and its coat will be lustrous. The condition of your dog's coat is one of the most visible indicators of health. If the coat is dull, chances are that your dog's metabolism is sluggish and unable to maintain vibrant health and a strong immune system. I know that if I miss a few days of the fatty acid source with my two dogs, their coats begin to lose their luster—a clear indication that they do better with a good supply of supplemented fatty acids.

BioFATS PROFILE

INGREDIENT	ACTIVE ELEMENT	BENEFIT
Fish oil blend	Rich supply of Omega 3 docosahexaenoic acid (DHA) (conditionally essential fatty acid)	DHA is primarily indicated for: neurological development and brain health improved cognition and learning capacity improved mood and behavior improved depression can improve temperament to mitigate aggression balanced prostaglandin hormone status anti inflammatory and pain control support of immune system health support of skin and coat health and related therapies combating insulin resistance and diabetes can support steroid therapies to reduce the quantity and duration of drug required
	Rich source of Omega 3 eicosapentaenoic acid (EPA) (conditionally essential fatty acid)	EPA is primarily indicated for: cardiovascular health, improving blood flow, clot control, cholesterol health, and heart rhythm neurological development and brain health improved cognition and learning capacity improved mood and behavior improved depression can improve temperament to mitigate aggression balanced prostaglandin hormone status anti inflammatory and pain control support of immune system health support of skin and coat health and related therapies can support steroid therapies to reduce the quantity and duration of drug required
Organic flaxseed oil	Supply of Omega 6 linoleic acid (LA) (essential fatty acid for dogs)	important precursor for prostaglandin hormones helps produce hormone balance between the Omega 3 derived hormones and the Omega 6 derived hormones partakes in smooth muscle regulation of intestines and blood vessels involved in neural impulse regulation

		precursor for the production of the Omega 3 ALA, DHA, and EPA in the cells involved in skin hydration and general health
	Supply of Omega 3 alpha linolenic acid (ALA) (conditionally essential fatty acid for dogs)	precursor for the production of DHA and EPA in the cells contributes to anti inflammatory activity
Virgin olive oil	Meager supply of Omega 6 linoleic acid (essential fatty acid for dogs)	important precursor for prostaglandin hormones helps produce hormone balance between the Omega 3 derived hormones and the Omega 6 derived hormones helps regulate smooth muscle of intestines and blood vessels involved in neural impulse regulation precursor for the production of Omega 3 ALA, DHA and EPA in the cells involved in skin hydration and general health
	Rich supply of Omega 9 monounsaturated fat	protects cardiovascular health by improving HDL (good cholesterol) to LDL (bad cholesterol) ratio
	Rich supply of polyphenols such as tyrosol and hydroxytyrosol antioxidants	potent antioxidant properties protecting the cells of the body and the fats within the body protect LDL from oxidation preserving blood vessel health protect the intestines from microbes and inflammation shown to improve gastritis and sooth ulcers of the stomach
Phosphatidylcholine	Healthy supply of lecithin	supports liver, brain and general health
Pancreatic Lipase	Digestive enzymes	enyzme specific to triglyceride digestion to support digestion and utilization of the important fatty acids
Natural preservation	Sage oleoresin, ascorbyl palmitate, mixed tocopherols	natural antioxidants that preserve the fatty acids in the bottle and serve as fat soluble antioxidants in the body

BioVITES

Essential fatty acids, supplied either in the form of food or supplements such as those in BIOFATS, must be delivered in the context of antioxidant support if they are to avoid oxidation and get their jobs done. This support comes in the form of nutrient cofactors such as vitamins A, C, and E (antioxidants); B vitamins; specific herbs (phytoantioxidants); and bioflavonoids. BIOVITES supplies these antioxidants, vitamins, minerals and other support nutrients and when added to a meal improves nutrient density and reduces the risk for nutrient deficiency. Although most good quality foods list an array of added nutrients on their labels, survival of these nutrients during processing and shelf storage is not guaranteed. Supplementation of every meal ensures these crucial essential nutrients are active and in sufficient levels at each meal.

BIOVITES is the second of the Nutritional Foundation products; together BIOFATS and BIOVITES deliver a powerful foundation for health. Individually they are powerful, but they each deliver a different benefit that supports the potential of the other.

BIOVITES is a vitamin and mineral powder that can protect the cells and the integrity of the fatty acids so they can do their work. Just like BIOFATS, BIOVITES also improves and protects insulin efficiency.

Protective support for fatty acids is the traditional job of antioxidants. However, antioxidants became news more recently because escalating levels of free radicals are doing oxidative damage to just about all living things at the cellular level. Practices in modern life have led to this escalation. In addition to free radical challenges from processed food, environmental challenges come in the form of the chemical load we have added to our environment. Some of these chemicals are daily household products. Others are common in the outdoors—in the air, water, and on the ground. Aside from the occasional accidental poisoning, everyone who lives in or around the home is exposed to these chemicals in small but frequent doses. We never know when family members, including our companion animals, will come in contact with man-made chemicals, including poisons.

KEY INGREDIENTS

One solution to the toxic challenge of the world around our pets is to use an antioxidant booster like Biovites. The formula includes a comprehensive vitamin blend, as well as manganese, zinc, and copper, which are important cofactors for the powerful superoxide dismutase (SOD), a potent antioxidant that helps prevent oxidative damage. In addition, manganese, zinc, copper, and sulphur assist in joint support and repair. Copper assists in hormone production and regulation; sulphur helps control inflammation. But these minerals are not necessarily helpers or facilitators of these specialized biological activities; they are merely essential components of the body's built-in systems that are involved in maintaining control over free radicals, recovery from wear-and-tear, and regulation of inflammation. Limited supply simply translates into limited activity of these important systems.

These minerals are in the Biovites formulation in the chelate form for easy absorption. The vitamins are presented in biologically active forms. This ensures maximum retention by the body for healthy bones and muscles, pH balance, and optimal metabolic activity. Biovites also provides a powerful array of digestive enzymes to support healthy digestion, healthy stomach pH, and clean teeth.

Biovites comes in a powdered form that can be blended with the dog food of your choice.

BioVITES PROFILE

INGREDIENT	ACTIVE ELEMENT	BENEFIT
Vitamin blend	Alpha tocopheryl succinate (vitamin E), ascorbic acid (vitamin C), thiamine hydrochloride (B1), riboflavin (B2), niacin (B3), pantothenic acid (B5) pyridoxine hydrochloride (B6), vitamin B12, coenzyme Q10, vitamin A palmitate, vitamin D_3, beta carotene, folic acid, biotin, inositol (B8)	essential vitamins crucial for healthy metabolism involved in energy (ATP) production from food cell membrane and organelle protection from free radicals antioxidant protection of the brain and body involved in neural impulse regulation and cognitive health bone, tooth, and gum development, maintenance and repair neurological development maintenance, and repair lean muscle development, maintenance, and repair skin and coat development, maintenance, and repair important cofactors in the metabolism of macronutrients such as protein, carbohydrate, and fat (including essential fatty acids)
Mineral blend	Calcium, magnesium, molybdenum, manganese, potassium, zinc, selenium, iodine, iron, copper, chromium	rich supply of minerals crucial for tissue building; tooth and bone health; muscle, ligament, cartilage and tendon integrity crucial electrolytes important for neurological health and impulse propagation partake in antioxidant support of the body critical to the natural clotting process, blood cell activity, enzyme regulation minerals are critical communication transmitters of a hormone's signal in the cells facilitate insulin activity; help with water regulation (osmotic gradients) and transfer in the body as well as temperature regulation involved in inflammatory regulation and pH balance
Phytonutrients	Atlantic kelp	supplies specialized minerals and nutrients in natural form to support thyroid
Specific amino acids	DL methionine, l taurine	methyl donor to protect DNA from activation of harmful genes supports insulin health and brain health, and provides immune system and lean muscle tissue fuels and nitrogen
Digestive	Lipase, protease	improves bioavailability of food

Enzymes	Bromelain, betain hydrochloride	increases nutrient absorption and feed efficiency
Food base carrier	Certified Organic Seed Blend (Flax, Sunflower, Sesame, Oat)	supplies key fatty acids, lignans, essential amino acids, and fiber in a food format to maximize bioavailability food base supports delivery of the purified isolated vitamins and minerals also supplied in this product

USING THE BIOLOGICVET FOUNDATION PROGRAM— BioFATS AND BioVITES

You can improve the nutrient density of a meal with the BiologicVET Foundation Program. Diets high in calories and low on nutrient density contribute to oxidation in the body and speed up biological aging. They may also make your dog fat, which can lead to a host of health problems. Yes, it is true that at the same time your dog is packing in the food, the animal may be undernourished.

Split the daily doses of BioFATS and BioVITES supplementation between the two regular feedings. Feeding two smaller meals daily as opposed to one larger meal is recommended. Follow the dosing instructions on the label of the BiologicVET product for either a saturation phase or a maintenance phase. The first few weeks of use of any BiologicVET product usually involve a saturation phase that brings the level of essential nutrients and antioxidants in the body and the cells to an optimal level. Once the cells are saturated, this state can be preserved using the maintenance level of dosing described on the label.

Is it possible to over-supplement?

Over-supplementation is only a problem if a single supplement or an incomplete combination of supplements is used aggressively. The lab tests that make the news with fresh discoveries of harmful effects are usually based on megadoses of a substance that is administered without including a proportional quantity of the necessary partner antioxidants. Confusion reigns in the public mind as brief reports in popular media fail to disclose all of the facts. Yes, toxic outcomes are possible when *any* substance is administered incorrectly and in very high doses, and that includes water.

BiologicVET nutraceutical formulations are complete, balanced products that fulfill co-dependent nutrient requirements. When added to feeds, this supplementation brings the feed's nutrient status closer to optimal nutrient proportions. Proper application is the key to a healthy outcome. Just administer the BiologicVET products as indicated on the label and know that the necessary synergies will happen. Results are noticeable in days.

BIOLOGIC NUTRITION
FROM PUPPYHOOD TO ADULTHOOD

The baseline integrity of a puppy's immune system and brain, plus general health in adulthood and senior years is determined by what the dog is fed in its early years.

A great example of this foundation is the growing neural network that requires an abundance of polyunsaturated fatty acids like DHA from the diet for optimal development.

In the case of the animal brain and neurons, they require an abundance of specialized fatty acid nutrients at developmental stages, but these are the delicate nutrients that are the first to be damaged (or removed) in the processing and storage of food. This nutrient damage can and will occur in other categories such as vitamins, minerals, and amino acids, but the essential fatty acids are the most vulnerable to damage by air, heat, and light exposure. Puppies need so much of the fatty-acid building blocks to set neurological structures and metabolic efficiency that regular diet alone—even if raw and whole—may not be able to meet the higher-than-normal demands. Boosting the best food you can find with supplemental sources of these essential and conditionally essential fatty acid building blocks ensures they are not limited in a puppy's food.

I suggest you use two different types of dry food to augment a primarily raw food diet for your young canine companion. One dry kibble might be a lamb base and the other a bison base. In the raw food category, I also choose two types. One might be a beef base and the other a chicken base with a different variety of vegetables for each. Getting your puppy accustomed to variety is important for future development. A varied diet provides a variety of nutrients from different sources, which will limit the risk of deficiency. It also provides an introduction to different foods so that your pet is less likely to be finicky in the future. The philosophy of feeding the same thing each day is extremely limited. Keep in mind that the kibble addition to these raw foods is to be a small sprinkling to just add some additional texture. The volume of this addition so small it should not influence the overall biological value of the meal.

Alternate the puppy's meals: feed the chicken-based raw food for a few days with sprinkled lamb kibble crunchies on it. Then switch to a different combination: for the next few days feed the beef-based raw food with bison kibble sprinkled on it. If raw food is not going to be the way you feed, just use a variety of dry and canned foods in much the same way. Add BiologicVET foundation supplements to each feed.

Ideally, puppies should start to get their fatty acid supplementation *in utero*, that is, throughout pregnancy, and then through suckling via their mother's milk feed. This requires that *Mom* gets these same supplements abundantly in her feed. Upon weaning, the fatty acid supplement in the food should be slowly introduced, according to label recommendation. Once the recommended dose of the fatty acid source (BioFATS for example) is reached and maintained for thirty days, begin to introduce a multivitamin and mineral supplement (BioVITES for example) in a slow, incremental fashion.

The recommended protocol for feeding adult dogs is not much different from feeding your puppy. Of course, the rate of development can slow down for adults, but the nutrient density of vitamins, minerals, antioxidants, and fatty acids must be supplied in abundance to maintain youth and preserve health. Here again, I recommend using a variety of feeds that provide a variety of nutrients. I prefer to use primarily a raw food diet and throw on a sprinkle of the common bagged, dry kibble, choosing a grain-free healthy version. On top of this, I add a multivitamin and mineral powder with a few squirts of BioFATS, which is a properly formulated fatty acid supplement produced with the ratios of Omega-3 to Omega-6 fatty acids that are specific to the dog. The species-specific ratio of fatty acids is critically important!

This supplementing strategy allows you to add joint support in the form of a joint supplement if the animal is suffering from joint ailments or is at risk of developing a related condition. If you have more than one dog, it also allows you to add other supplements, which may be condition-specific, to one pet's food, while allowing the other pet in the family to eat the same base feed and base foundation supplements (vitamin-mineral and fatty acid).

Dogs age faster than humans, and they seem to age at an even faster rate in their later years. Your canine companion might decline in general wellness more from the age of nine (human years) to fourteen years than they do from ages four to nine. However, despite your dog's chronological age, you can use nutrition and other lifestyle modifications to lower your pet's biological age.

As your dog advances in years, the damage due to oxidation accumulates, and health maintenance systems in the body become less efficient and more vulnerable to damage from environmental toxins and invading microbes. Often, what is perceived as disease in an older dog is simply slow recovery from daily wear-and-tear. Natural antioxidant production in your pets' cells declines as your pet ages, and dietary fatty acids can be compromised before they get to cells. This means you need to supplement the diet with an array of antioxidants that the body can easily digest and absorb to compensate for this internal decline. BioVITES can provide those antioxidants. Senior pets are also less efficient at making the non-essential fatty acids such as ALA, DHA and EPA, and they can benefit from supplementation of BioFATS.

Other changes associated with aging include less efficient digestion as the gastrointestinal tract experiences wear-and-tear, as well as reduced insulin efficiencies that affect metabolism. These changes will compromise the absorption of nutrients. Muscle wasting is also experienced by aging pets. This decline is so reliably consistent that lean muscle mass is one of the markers used to assess biological age. Loss of lean muscle increases the risk of disease and contributes to physical aging because it robs the body of its site and source of glutamine and branched-chain amino acids, which are key fuels for the immune system. In times of desperation, the body will use these special immune system fuels from the muscle and if this reservoir is already depleted, recovery from illness can be slow. The depletion of muscle in elderly humans and animals is, in part, due to the extraction of immune system fuels and building blocks from the lean tissues. Lack of physical activity also contributes to this muscle atrophy.

BioSENIOR

BioSENIOR adds an anti-aging strategy to the combination of BioFATS and BioVITES, the two foundation products. This supplement is designed for animals five years or older needing a metabolic lift or for convalescing animals requiring recovery support. BioSENIOR was designed to improve the ability of the cells to recycle their energy source, adenosine triphosphate (ATP). As our pets age, ATP is recycled at a slower rate in the cells and this, in part, contributes to a slower recovery from day-to-day wear-and-tear. (The same applies to you and me.) BioSENIOR includes ingredients that improve ATP status of the heart muscle, neural network, and skeletal muscles. Energy enhancement is immediately noticeable, and the body is better able to keep up with maintenance of tissues and important hormones.

KEY INGREDIENTS

The BioSENIOR formulation is designed to support a healthy heart, mental alertness and acuity and muscle energy. This formula additionally improves hydration and muscle tone and strength. BioSENIOR supplies glutamine, methylsulfonylmethane, and a potent array of digestive enzymes to facilitate nutrient digestibility and the building of muscle. These nutrients support the muscle mass to prevent the destruction and premature atrophy of the tissue. In addition, the formulation includes creatine, coenzyme Q10, and other antioxidants that support heart health, gums, cognition, and muscle strength. BioSENIOR turns back the clock.

BioSENIOR PROFILE

INGREDIENT	ACTIVE CONSTITUENT	BENEFIT
Vitamin enhancement	Coenzyme Q10	healthy CoQ10 serving to support energy production and connective tissues, including gums
Mineral blend	Methylsulfonlymethane, chromium	supplies supplemental highly bioavailable sulfur and chromium—two elements that are more difficult for seniors to acquire and require in higher dietary intakes to meet demands supports coat, nails, bone, muscle, and insulin health maximizes metabolism of nutrients needed for energy and strength
Energy and lean muscle support	Creatine monohydrate	improves nitrogen retention in muscles enhances muscle hydration, tone, strength, and stamina improves ability to recycle the cell's prime energy source (ATP) delivers anti inflammatory and antioxidant activity improves energy status of the brain and neurons improves protein synthesis for tissue recovery improves feed efficiency to maximize nutrient retention
Herbal support	Bladderwrack, grapeseed extract	improves thyroid efficiency to maximize metabolism designed to reduce levels of inflammatory prostaglandin hormones spares vitamin C so it is more readily available as an antioxidant
Specific amino acids	L glutamine, l cystine, l taurine	improves insulin health so nutrients can be conveyed to tissues more readily supports anti inflammatory activity and glutathione antioxidant status to neutralize free radicals produced during physical work provides immune system and lean muscle tissue fuels improves nitrogen retention of lean muscle protects intestinal lining; enhances growth hormone status

| Digestive enzymes | Bromelain, papain, pancreatic lipase | improves bioavailability of food increases nutrient absorption and transport of critical nutrients provides additional anti inflammatory activity to improve recovery from physical work improves feed efficiency |
| Food base carrier | Certified Organic Seed Blend (Flax, Sunflower, Sesame, Oat) | supplies key fatty acids, lignans, essential amino acids and fiber in a food format to maximize bioavailability food base supports delivery of the purified isolated vitamins and minerals also supplied in this product |

BioSENIOR does not supply the building blocks for joint tissue or the chondrocyte activators required for collagen synthesis. However, it does support joint recovery through different pathways. (For information about a supplement specifically made for joint support, see BioJOINT in Chapter 5.)

The Nutritional Foundation products, BioFATS and BioVITES, provide all the essential nutrients in abundance, and they should be used to provide a solid foundation that BioSENIOR can build on. However, BioSENIOR can rejuvenate very effectively on its own, if you decide to use it exclusively.

My canine companions, Dexter and Diesel are in their senior years. I feed them a varied, carefully balanced raw food diet. In addition, they get BioVITES, the nutrient-rich vitamin/mineral powder that also has a potent dose of phytoantioxidants.

Dexter and Diesel both get an additional senior supplement, BioSENIOR, since one of them, Diesel, is thirteen human years of age and the other, Dexter, is sixteen human years of age. My newest addition (about a year ago) to the pack is my beefy Rottweiler Lennox. Lennox 'the champ' is now weighing in at a monstrous 135–137 lean pounds and at this weight, he is able to keep up on bike rides and runs at least four times per week. Lennox is a formidable canine. The food and supplements are mixed into the bowl to make a yummy slurry they willingly gulp down. Dexter and Diesel look great, and they bound around the yard like puppies, outrunning and out-muscling younger animals they play with. This quality nutrition is the foundation of their youthful physical and mental state.

Lennox, our Rottweiler boy, came to us when he was about 1.5 years old. His coat, muscle tone and general health were amazing and one couldn't imagine his conditioning being any better the day we adopted him. However, once his nutritional program incorporated the BiologicVET strategies, his coat became even more lustrous and amazingly thicker and hardy. He was at the age where we expected more muscle development and filling out to come in the next few years. However, within a matter of ONLY three weeks, he looked so much more muscled and what we thought to be a lazy demeanour or personality turned suddenly into a frolicking, bounding animal full of bustling work drive.

Today, this 137 pound boy is one of the most awe inspiring animals I've ever had as part of the family. It's a good thing he's gentle, confident and respectful of his place in the family pack. Lennox is a good example of an animal that MUST be regularly reminded of his place in the family hierarchy through stern, confident and clear but always respectful and healthy correction in order to safeguard everyone including him. And he must take part in regular exercise to allow for that energy and the herding and protection instincts to be used to build a healthy mind and body instead of allowing it to become pent up to fester increasing the risk for disease and exploding as an unexpected reaction.

Dexter's Nutritional Program

16-year-old Terrier-Shepherd Cross; lean 74 lbs (34 kg); joint discomfort related to a historical leg injury and subsequent surgery after rescue

Fed twice a day with a raw food diet sprinkled with some kibble. The raw food is sometimes chicken and veggies; other times beef and veggies with fruit; other times bison and greens. The kibble source is also varied but always grain-free. The addition of the kibble is primarily as a texture modifier, and the volume is so small it does not influence the overall biological value of the meal that much.

Each meal is supplemented as follows:

- BioFATS: 3-5 pumps
- BioVITES: 3-4 scoops
- BioJOINT: 2-3 scoops every second day (on the days BioSENIOR is not supplemented)
- BioSENIOR: 1-2 scoops every second day (on the days BioJOINT is not supplemented)
- Dexter gets BioSPORT in his food in place of BioSENIOR once per week.
- Dexter gets one whole raw egg, one day each week.

I also make certain the protein* intake is optimized by adding a highly purified whey peptide fraction powder to one meal per day; to support immunity and anabolism and reduce the risk for muscle wasting (sarcopenia) at his age.

Diesel's Nutritional Program

13-year-old Jack Russell Terrier; lean 24 lbs (11 kg)

Fed twice a day with raw food diet sprinkled with some grain-free kibble. Raw food is sometimes chicken and veggies; other times beef and veggies with fruit; other times bison and greens.

Each Meal is supplemented as follows:

- BioFATS: 2-3 pumps
- BioVITES: 1-2 scoops
- BioJOINT: 1 scoop every second day (on the days BioSENIOR is not supplemented)
- Diesel gets one whole raw egg, one day each week.

I also make certain the protein* intake is optimized by adding a highly purified whey peptide fraction powder to one meal per day; to support immunity and anabolism and reduce the risk for muscle wasting (sarcopenia) at his age.

Lennox's Nutritional Program
2.5-year-old Purebred Rottweiler; lean 135-137 lbs (62 kg)
Fed twice a day with raw food diet sprinkled with some grain-free kibble. Raw food is sometimes chicken and veggies; other times beef and veggies with fruit; other times bison and greens.
Each Meal is supplemented as follows:
- BioFATS: 5-6 pumps
- BioVITES: 3-4 scoops
- BioJOINT: 1-2 scoops two times per week
- BioSPORT: 2-3 scoops per meal
- Lennox gets one whole raw egg, approximately two days each week.

I also make certain the protein* intake is optimized by adding a highly purified whey peptide fraction powder to both meals per day; to support immunity and anabolism of this growing active animal.

*This incremental unflavored PLAIN peptide powder of extremely high biological value (BV>135) helps foster maximum drive, immunity, cognitive function, energy and metabolic efficiency. This strategy is especially valuable for working/sporting animals allowing for fortification with precious protein/peptide building blocks and energy substrates void of Advanced Glycosylated Endproducts (AGES defined on page 48) that unfortunately are formed due to oxidative reactions when dog food is processed under extreme conditions. Contrary to common belief, elevated dietary protein is beneficial and not necessarily harmful unless the AGE content is high in the protein fraction of the food due to processing as described in earlier pages. More canine-dietary protein research posted at *http://www.biologicnr.com/2170*.

FOUR

PHSYICAL ACTIVITY:
ESSENTIAL FOR VITALITY

Physical exercise maintains health and helps preserve youthful characteristics in both human and animal members of the family. Research has produced credible evidence that using regular resistance training to maintain muscle mass and stimulating the cardiovascular system with a regular brisk walk or light run will support longevity and improved quality of life. This doesn't mean you need to set your dog up on a weight training program with a personal trainer. It does, however, mean that you need to allow your pet a regular, brisk run on some variable terrain that includes declines and inclines. This challenges muscles to maintain their youthful size and functional strength. It also stimulates the maintenance of bone mass, maintains the health of connective tissue, and stimulates lymphatic activity that helps detoxify the body. (This information applies to your dog, you, and your family members.)

THE BENEFITS
OF PHYSICAL ACTIVITY

The old cliché "use it or lose it" definitely applies when it comes to animal muscle strength and muscle tone. Sedentary lifestyles contribute to the degeneration of body tissues known as lean body mass, which is mostly muscle and bone. This loss of lean tissue is known as sarcopenia. Muscles are more metabolically active than most other tissues so when the muscle mass is fit and robust, it is using calories efficiently to help manage body fat and support other processes. Less muscle translates into less immune support and poorer energy management. A body that is fit can actually metabolize more food calories instead of storing them as fat. This translates into more energy and more nutrients for general body maintenance. Poor muscle tone and health usually means even less physical activity, and the pattern of inactivity can become a downward spiral of decreasing muscle mass and ever-decreasing energy levels, activity, and health.

As you and your dog age, lean-muscle mass tends to diminish naturally. As noted, this decline is so consistent that muscle mass is a reliable marker to assess biological age. An increase in fat mass is also one of those markers used to evaluate biological age, and quite often a decrease in muscle mass is accompanied by an increase in body fat—but not because one turns into the other. If humans lose muscle, the risk of disease increases and the potential to recover from disease declines. The same is true for other animals, including our companion canines and felines. If regular exercise isn't part of your pet's lifestyle today, you should add it immediately, even if it's just one brisk 20-minute walk each day. (And yes, the rest of the family will benefit if they come along.) After "a certain age," both pets and humans must work to maintain the muscle mass they have. Physical exercise preserves youthful muscle.

In the case of your companion canine, resistance training may involve hill climbing, hill descent, tug-of-war, and simple chewing on bones as a snack for physical exercise. Tug-of-war must be carefully managed to avoid harming the neck of smaller breeds. You should also take care to maintain your balance and control during a tug-of-war activity with a dominant animal that may play the game too hard. Games that involve power and competition can be viewed by dominant dogs as challenges for dominant position of the pack.

Make pet toys for play available on a rotation, changing up the availability so pets don't become bored with the same old play things. After play time with your dog is over, praise and reward with a special but healthy food treat. Play time is crucial for everyone's physical and mental health.

> *Exercise for Arthritis*
> Contrary to conventional thinking, exercise is important even if your dog is contending with disease, including arthritis. The endorphin secretions triggered by regular, controlled exercise actually help ease pain. The alternative is a sedentary lifestyle that contributes to further degeneration of tissues and increased inflammation.

Regular physical activity also improves health conditions related to insulin resistance and diabetes. Challenging muscles with physical work prompts healthy hormonal activity. It's part of the natural mechanism whereby the body attempts to adapt to physical work by improving nutrient absorption by the cells. Consequently, sugar transport for energy required by the working cells improves, helping rejuvenate insulin efficiency and correct a diabetic condition. Reduction of insulin resistance enhances general health and lowers biological age.

This improved hormone efficiency also enhances metabolic health and lowers the risk for cardiovascular disease and even obesity while exercise improves heart, lung, and vascular conditioning. Exercise is the elixir of health. Sedentary lifestyles impair life.

Exercise pumps toxins out of the body

The heart pumps blood and nutrients to organs and the periphery of the body, but there's no automatic system that pumps toxins out of the body with the same effectiveness. The lymphatic system maintains the balance of fluids in the body, and circulating lymph (a fluid) helps eliminate metabolic byproducts and toxins that the cells of the body are bathed in.

The lymphatic system is powered by working muscles. Therefore, a sedentary lifestyle slows the flow of fluid and allows cellular sludge to accumulate and impair the cells. Physically working muscle tissue helps pump this toxicity out of the body, supporting health and vigor. This is one reason we feel better and more mentally alert when we exercise regularly. The muscles act like pumps to promote lymphatic circulation, and they push lymph throughout the body, continuing the flow to lymph nodes where immune system defenders destroy pathogens and metabolic byproducts are detoxified.

The alternative to all this activity is a sedentary lifestyle that could lead to muscle atrophy. At the same time, adipose tissue, which contributes to obesity and an increased risk for diabetes, bone disease, cancer, depression, dementia and more, is likely to flourish. Increases in your pet's body fat promote that previously discussed underlying cellular inflammation that increases the risk for illness and premature aging. Physical activity helps maintain healthy body fat status.

If your dog lacks energy and work drive, fortifying food with a bit of the peptide that is described on page 96 to improve protein quantity and quality of the meal will help with energy, drive and recovery without the risk associated with AGES.

If your pet is active on a regular basis and gets the right polyun-saturated fats and other important antioxidants from the diet, health maintenance and recovery from disease can be easy. An arthritic con-dition will improve with relative ease if the right nutritional supplements are taken while engaging in controlled activity. The right nutritional program will trigger the regeneration of cartilage despite the physical activity. Glucosamine on its own cannot accomplish this regeneration; not for osteoarthritis and definitely not for rheumatoid arthritis. For complete information on nutritional supplements to ease arthritis, see BioJOINT in Chapter 5.

IS IT PLAY OR IS IT WORK?

If you and your pet are inactive, getting started will be your biggest challenge. This is like altering the course of a supertanker. It's no dif-ferent for your own state of health. Your pet's state of health will like-ly mirror your own, and so you and your pet might be able to embark on a rejuvenation and regeneration program together. Using the right supplements, and a safe and moderate exercise program, health can be re-established; health and quality of life can be maintained life-long.

Playing tug-of-war in your backyard is a safe way to bond as well as build and maintain your dog's muscle mass. Again, caution is required to ensure that the activity is not too aggressive. As much as their teeth are incredibly strong, we mustn't push them hard enough to cause tooth, gum, or neck injury, especially in the case of older animals.

Playing catch or fetch is obviously the favorite pastime of most dogs. Find a slight incline, not too steep, and play a few throws of fetch with this extra load to challenge the muscles. If your animal is too old or vulnerable to hip weakness, be careful not to choose inclines that are too steep. A few light hill climbs will suffice in the case of gen-eral health maintenance for both of you.

Daily maintenance of health will not require much intensity, and a brisk walk on the level field with some added brief hill climbs may be enough each day. Keep in mind that our animals may play to please us to their detriment. This is definitely the case when it comes to my Staffordshire-Terrier cross. (Labrador Retrievers are also known to play fetch in the hot sun until they collapse.) Know their limits and play within them. My Jack Russell will hide his ball when he has had enough.

I no longer train my dogs to compete in racing, hurdles, and agility, so I simply run with them three to four times a week for about four to eight kilometers each time. A few hills may get in the way, and I'll take them fast on a good day and walk them or run them slowly on a day when we're just not up to it. You and your pet will have your own comfort level when it comes to level and intensity of activity, but don't be afraid to challenge that from time to time. You'll be pleasantly surprised by how quickly the two of you can build some stamina and strength.

FINDING SAFE PLACES TO PLAY

I worry about allowing my dogs to run free even in "off-leash" parks. One never knows what the curious canines will get into. When I do allow them to be free, I always keep them in sight. Other leashed dogs may not be as comfortable or confident as your dog might be on leash and may react aggressively to oncoming off-leash animals.

Always be aware of the condition of the park you and your pet are exercising in. Even if it appears to be well groomed and weed-free, caution is in order because chemicals might be used as part of the maintenance program. Exercising on the golf course before or after hours is an emphatic no-no. The chemicals used to maintain the greens are enough to limit my own recreational indulgence. I wouldn't want my children playing on this potential toxin source either. If a dog is running around, collecting chemicals from these pesticide-laden greens, he'll take them home to contaminate the carpets, furniture, and floors where the children play as well.

It's also dangerous to allow a dog to run free in the forest in the evening due to the possibility of an attack by coyotes, even in urban areas. Your canine companion may be a big and strong breed, but, unlike your family pet, coyotes kill for a living and they're good at it. Your relatively naive pet is an easy target for them. Coyotes and wolves are clever hunters and will lure your male into the forest with the scent of the pack's female as bait. Your unsuspecting pet can fall prey to the ambush of several coyotes. On separate occasions, I've seen large breeds such as a healthy strong Shepherd and a good size Dalmatian narrowly miss being completely ripped apart. The Dalmatian escaped with a torn belly that almost lost its contents before arriving home in time for an emergency veterinary visit.

Porcupines can cause painful injuries to curious dogs. (The quills are best dealt with by an experienced vet.) Encounters with skunks are not dangerous but pose other problems for pet owners. Theories on how to get rid of the smell are plentiful, but I have yet to hear of a fool-proof one. (The same goes for cleaning up dogs who can't resist rolling in that dead fish on the beach.) An animal that's used to being in the house may have to be banned for several days, which is a distressing experience for a pet used to lots of attention and affection.

Farmer's fields should be out of bounds as well. Farmers will often use bait and traps to deter coyotes and other vermin that destroy their crops. Insecticides are also commonly used in these fields and will accumulate in puddles of water. Your dog needs to stay clear of these fields for its own safety but also to respect the farmer's livelihood.

The safest place to exercise your pet is at the end of a leash while on a brisk walk or run; at a naturally maintained off-leash park, running the hills in a game of catch-and-fetch; within sight while walking or running the off-leash park trails; or in the backyard.

TRAINING DOGS FOR COMPETITIVE SPORT

When I trained my Jack Russell for his racing events, most of the training was done on hills. I simply went for a brisk jog with him for fifteen to twenty minutes to arrive at the park. Then, I ran some hills with him—sprinting up and then walking down. He loved it! I would then urge him to do some mild hill climbs on his own since he could outrun me up those hills.

A game of hill-fetch also worked well. I threw his favorite ball with the assistance of a tennis racket or a ball flinger. Then I moved to two or three climbs of about fifty yards or so up a steep fifty-degree incline. The hill climb training may have taken a total of five to ten minutes—four or five throws up the mild incline, and four or five throws up the steeper one. On most occasions, I just ran up the steeper inclines to engage in interval training, running shorter climbs than my off-leash dog. This would give him the needed freedom to push as hard as he could to keep with the rhythm for his training. We'd run as fast as we could up the hill and walk down. Dogs love the friendly competition, and they love even more to beat the pants off you as they pass you going up the hill after their ball. Repeat it a few times. It's great health building for both of you. Keep in mind though, that the intense hill climbs are intended to build competitive strength, and they are not needed if basic health maintenance is the objective.

When we were done, we'd run back home or if we felt a bit spent, we'd walk home briskly. Too much work can backfire to burn out and strain the body and increase the risk of injury and illness. We'd execute this program every second day, with the alternating day involving a slow-paced run or fast-paced walk. Remember, this was a training program for sport.

If your dog is highly active and you both enjoy competition, you may consider training for events such as flyball, agility, racing, field trials, and even old-fashioned hunting. Dog groups involved in local and international competition in these different fields are easily accessible through Internet searches.

In competition, the performance difference between first and second place is often so fine it's next to impossible to differentiate. Many elements factor into the winning strategy, including genetics, training technique, discipline, iron will, and nutrition. Many of us, from weekend warriors to professional human athletes and guardians of professional animal athletes in sport, work hard to master each component of this winning formula, but few have a deep understanding of the nutritional factor. No amount of discipline, training, or genetics can compensate for poor nutrition. Performance potential is proportionally limited or enhanced by nutritional status.

Great genetics combined with poor nutrition results in performance levels short of genetic potential. In addition, research demonstrates that poor nutrition combined with rigorous exercise is a recipe for injury and disease. Athletes and their canine companions should nourish themselves with high-performance fuel, the same way a champion driver fuels a performance car for competition. Low-grade fuel will slow down both the car and the canine. The harder we push the performance machine on sub-par fuel, the more oxidative wear the body experiences while underperforming. The more active a body is, the more free radicals are produced, and, therefore, more antioxidants are needed to neutralize them.

Your canine athlete needs higher levels of protective nutrition than less active animals so first and foremost, choose a high-quality feed that supplies a great nutritional foundation. Simply supplying more of the same (possibly) nutritionally deficient feed will not meet the higher micronutrient demands of the canine athlete's body. More food only delivers more crude calories for the body to work through to extract nutrition. Good quality, bioavailable vitamin, mineral, fatty acid, and antioxidant supplementation that can enter the cells easily makes the best contribution to the digestion and use of food nutrients.

BioSPORT

BioSPORT has been formulated to contribute to optimal performance while it protects health. It boosts strength, muscle size and tone, speed, and endurance. BioSPORT's performance nutrients increase feed efficiency and improve the food's energy potential. These nutrients also improve the cells' ability to recycle energy sources for quick recovery. It supports insulin efficiency to assist in recovery from exercise by keeping inflammation in check.

When it comes to competitive sport, if you're not paying close attention to nutritional detail, your dog will lose every time to a canine athlete whose owner is. But just as much as these nutrients can enhance athletic performance and accelerate recovery from physical work, they protect your dog's body from the physical wear incurred by the extra work. In fact, many of these so-called sports supplements used today by human, canine, equine, and other athletes are widely used in medicine to assist recovery of the body during the treatment of disease.

KEY INGREDIENTS

Along with pre-digested plant nutrition and other good things found in the wild, the ancestors of today's domestic dogs got a good supply of **creatine** from the muscle meat of wild animals every time they made a fresh kill. Coyotes, wolves, wild dogs, and other wild carnivores of today still get this higher creatine load in their wild kill and this creatine, in turn, supports the strength, speed, and recovery they need to chase down the prey. The muscle meat consumed by animals dining in the wild can have as much as five (and even eight) times the amount of creatine found in the highly processed, farmed meat of domesticated animals. Physical activity also generates creatine in the cells, and today's dogs get little chance to make creatine and build their muscles, despite the best intentions of their owners. (That said, if given a choice, few modern dogs would opt for a life in the wild.)

If the creatine in a dog's body is depleted due to poor dietary supply and low levels of activity, its muscle tone will decline. This is one reason why animals in the wild usually have more strength per pound than domestic animals. The sub-par energy system of domestic dogs has implications that go deeper than just muscle strength. Brain activity, heart efficiency, and even joint health are all affected by a shortfall of creatine. Creatine is also known to deliver anti-inflammatory activity and antioxidant protection.

If a dog's creatine is depleted due to poor dietary supply, muscle tone declines, and mental and physical energy and strength are reduced as well. However, in order for creatine supplementaion to deliver expected performance enhancements such as better stamina, muscle tone, and jumping or pulling power, it has to be administered correctly. Even this proven performance booster is useless unless combustion-controlling micronutrients—vitamins, minerals, and antioxidants—accompany it in proportional amounts. Some of these key cofactors are included in the proper context in the formula. A more complete supply of the cofactors is offered in BioVITES. BioVITES serves as a perfect synergistic adjunct to BioSPORT for animals involved in rigorous physical activity programs. If administered on its own, results from BioSPORT will be impressive, but if it is administered with all of its cofactor nutrition—with BioVITES—the health and performance results will be incredible.

BiosPORT also includes a potent dose of digestive enzymes and natural fibers that feed the friendly bacteria in the gut. Glutamine is supplied in this formula to support glutathione status. Glutathione is a powerful antioxidant that helps detoxify the entire body and support immune system activity.

BIOSPORT PROFILE

INGREDIENT	ACTIVE ELEMENTS	BENEFIT
Mineral blend	Methylsulfonlymethane, chromium	maximizes performance and recovery from physical work helps retain hydration designed to optimize pH
Performance enhancement	Creatine monohydrate	improves nitrogen retention in muscles enhances muscle hydration, tone, strength, and stamina improves ability to recycle the cell's prime energy source (ATP) delivers anti inflammatory and antioxidant activity improves energy status of the brain and neurons improves protein synthesis for tissue recovery and lean tissue restoration and rebuilding improves feed efficiency to maximize nutrient retention
Herbal support	Bladderwrack	improves thyroid efficiency to maximize energy and lean body mass health
Specific amino acids	L glutamine	improves insulin health and delivery of nutrients supports anti inflammatory activity and glutathione antioxidant status to neutralize free radicals produced during physical work provides immune system and lean muscle tissue fuels improves nitrogen retention of lean muscle protects intestinal lining helps maximize natural growth hormone status

Digestive enzymes	Bromelain	improves bioavailability of food increases nutrient absorption and transport of critical nutrients; also provides additional anti inflammatory activity to improve recovery from physical work; improves feed efficiency
Food base carrier	Certified Organic Seed Blend (Flax, Sunflower, Sesame, Oat)	supplies key fatty acids, lignans, essential amino acids, and fiber in a food format to maximize bioavailability food base supports delivery of the purified isolated vitamins and minerals also supplied in this product

I even feed my less active older dogs BIOSPORT at least once and some-times a few times each week simply because it supplies the level of cre-atine they would get if they were eating wild meat. And although BIOSPORT is a comprehensive design that delivers formidable perform-ance results on its own, the overall effect and health potential for your dog will be further enhanced by the concurrent use of BIOFATS and BIOVITES (the Nutritional Foundation).

Since a dog's metabolism runs a little faster than a human's, your dog will experience benefits from dietary changes and supplement addi-tions more quickly than you might—you should see some surprising results after the fifth or sixth day of use. Muscle strength, tone, and size, as well as stamina and speed build within days to deliver jaw-dropping results! Results will improve as the product is used for longer terms. Since the formula is designed to improve protein synthesis and recovery of muscle from work, the formulation will progressively advance strength and stamina to maximize your athlete's genetic performance potential safely. Improving protein status of the feed as described on page 96 will also provide huge energy, performance and recovery bene-fits as well as immune system function and healthy aging.

FIVE

COMBATING COMMON CANINE HEALTH PROBLEMS

Despite all the care and attention from owners, puppies and older companion animals can be more vulnerable to health problems. Minor scrapes and injuries can be treated from the first aid kit. Major health crises—serious injuries and illnesses—require the attention of a skilled vet.

With the foundation supplements BIOVITES and BIOFATS, you can improve health at the cellular level. This in turn will improve the animal's physical ability to regenerate new cells and tissue and fortify your dog's immune system against infection. Nevertheless, curious canines out in the world will encounter places and things that they can't resist sniffing, tasting, eating, or rolling in. An active life will trigger wear-and-tear on joints and muscles despite the general health it promotes. An inactive life will lead to obesity and all the health problems that are made worse by a high level of body fat, including insulin resistance, increased risk of inflammation and infection, and even diabetes. Balance is the key to optimal health.

Beyond the foundation products for optimal pet health, the

BiologicVET program offers three specific products for three specific conditions. BioJOINT can be used to treat arthritis and related joint problems. BioSLIM will help you tackle and reduce your dog's high levels of body fat and reduce the strain on joints and organs that too much weight imposes. BioSKIN&COAT will help your pet's body combat common skin problems that are usually the result of coming into contact with irritants that trigger an inaccurate or exaggerated immune-system response. This might involve a mild reaction such as itching or a severe reaction that results in bloody sores.

ARTHRITIS

Arthritis refers to as many as 100 different diseases affecting the area in or around a body's joints. Arthritis is not only crippling an aging human population, it's also assaulting our pets at an extraordinary rate. There are breed-specific genetic vulnerabilities to arthritis, but if the maintenance systems in the dog's body stay in good form, premature cartilage wear—osteoarthritis—can be avoided.

Not surprisingly, nutrition can play a huge role in advancing or preventing joint disease related to wear-and-tear. A diet that supplies healthy collagen building blocks like glucosamine and glycosaminoglycans will be more likely to forestall the early onset of osteoarthritis than a diet that relies on heavily processed foods. To further compound matters, a diet that is processed to the point where fatty acids and amino acids are damaged will actually contribute to oxidation and inflammation in the body and interfere with the body's ability to use those cartilage building blocks to repair joint tissues.

A raw food diet, on the other hand, supplies natural building blocks for collagen. This natural supply of glycosaminoglycans and other cartilage nutrients provides fabulous support and protection for joints on a day-to-day basis. Additionally, this whole food does not present the same oxidative potential in the body, eliminating the interference that commonly impairs the body's ability to restore health after wear and tear has taken its toll.

After the onset of osteoarthritis, however, a pharmacological effect that re-activates collagen manufacturing in the damaged joints is required. The dog's body needs a supply of active nutritional ingredients that have been engineered to penetrate to the cartilage cells themselves—the chondrocytes—to reactivate them.

The chondrocytes are the worker cells of the cartilage tissue or matrix, as it's often referred to, that use glucosamine to make collagen. Collagen and other compounds, referred to as proteoglycans and glycosaminoglycans, also make up the cartilage tissue, lending it that rubbery characteristic. In order for the chondrocytes to make and preserve functional cartilage tissue they need minerals like sulphur, copper, and manganese, and vitamins like C, D, and E to name just a few. The wear and tear of time and use can cause these worker cells to become dormant. Even if these nutrients were supplied abundantly by the diet, the joint tissue could not be constructed without the activity of the chondrocyte.

The oxidation that can escalate in our senior animals also interferes with the activity of the chondrocyte. Since our pets' protective antioxidant systems degrade as they age, oxidant interference with the work of the chondrocytes goes unchallenged. Even dogs on a raw food diet will need extra support in the form of chondrocyte activators as they age. Food alone, even if it is fresh and whole, cannot accomplish the task.

Supplementation of the raw food diet with nutrients that can protect chondrocytes and reactivate them when they have become dormant is essential if joint tissue is to be regenerated. Fortified dry feeds, such as those commonly packaged in bags, also need added supplements that provide support and recovery potential. As discussed, many of the nutrients added back to these feeds in the form of fortification cannot survive in the bag long-term while stored on the store shelf or at your home. Some condition-specific diets will supply joint building blocks in the feed such as glucosamine, but these processed and then fortified feeds are still not as good as engineered compounds created to get a specific job done. They do not provide the keys that turn on dormant chondrocytes or keep them in the "on" position as our animals age. In addition, these feeds rarely detail how much glucosamine, chondroitin, antioxidants, and other important joint nutrients might be added to the feed and what form they are in. In fact, because they are highly processed, these bagged and canned feeds contribute to general body oxidation, further interfering with chondrocyte activity and preventing the added nutrients from delivering their benefits.

BioJOINT

BioJOINT is a blend of joint-friendly vitamins and minerals and cartilage-specific factors, supported by anti-inflammatory herbs and amino acids and digestive enzymes. This specialized joint support combats inflammation to reduce pain and swelling and improve mobility and flexibility. It is designed to penetrate to the genetic level and activate the body's ability to literally regenerate cartilage tissue and repair worn and torn joints. It's what we call an 'active' joint formula and not just a passive supply of joint ingredients.

The cartilage building blocks come in the form of glucosamine sulphate potassium chloride, chondroitin sulphate, and glucosamine hydrochloride. Careful product design of this nutrient support is critical because the size of the molecules used to deliver glucosamine building blocks and glycosaminoglycans has a major influence on whether or not the compounds make their way to the joint tissue at concentrations high enough to make a difference. That's right, not all glucosamines are the same nor are all types of chondroitin. BioJOINT uses low-molecular weight ingredients to deliver a very powerful result. The ingredients are engineered to penetrate faster and deeper. Its ingredients are delivered in a powder form to ensure maximum absorption in the dog's fast-moving, relatively shorter (shorter than a human's) gastrointestinal tract.

KEY INGREDIENTS

Research has shown that chondrocytes in diseased arthritic tissue produce more nitric oxide than chondrocytes in healthy cartilage do. Excess nitric oxide can breed an overload of free radicals—the nasty peroxynitrite free radical, to be specific. It also interferes with the chondrocytes' regeneration of collagen in cases of osteoarthritis.

A 2001 Spanish study to determine which compounds worked best on damaged joints tested ways to reduce the nitric oxide, using glucosamine hydrochloride, Type II collagen, chondroitin sulphate, and glucosamine sulphate—compounds that are all sold in most health-food stores. Of all the compounds tested on human and canine tissue, chondroitin sulphate showed the best results. It was the only one that seemed to be able to reduce nitric oxide in arthritic tissues and improve the construction of joint tissue proteoglycans and hyaluronic acid. The result is a natural anti-inflammatory effect and reconstruction of the cartilage matrix.

When it comes to chondroitin, the size of the molecule plays a central role in how effective it can be. Large molecules from crude chondroitin sources cannot penetrate to the cartilage tissue to deliver its pharmacological result. Low molecular weight (chondroitin chain length engineered to be smaller or shorter) material delivers the protective and activation properties.

The sulphate form is a key as well—sulphur is another critical factor in the manufacture of cartilage tissue or matrix. The sulphur group plays two roles in natural therapy: it supplies the sulphur needed for the protein cross-linking that gives cartilage its rubbery, shock-absorbing collagen, and it acts as a powerful antioxidant that helps regulate nitric oxide, peroxynitrite, and other free radicals.

In the past, research on chondroitin's effectiveness has produced inconsistent results. The conflicting results are related to the quality of compounds used in the studies and the intestinal health of the subjects. Bigger chondroitin molecules produce less reliable results. The chondroitin source in BioJOINT is a low-molecular weight compound—a short chain. This means that the chondroitin in BioJOINT can be absorbed efficiently by the gut, through a process called pinocytosis, delivering site-specific nitric-oxide regulation and site-specific antioxidant potential.

Another key ingredient is glucosamine. Glucosamine hydrochloride, which has become the common alternative treatment for joint disease, does not supply the necessary sulphur. It can deliver a little more glucosamine per gram than glucosamine sulphate simply because it has a little more glucosamine in the molecule, but that doesn't mean the nutrient gets used to build tissue. The lack of sulphur results in limited conversion of the glucosamine building blocks to collagen or cartilage matrix tissue.

BioJOINT is a comprehensive formula that supplies a variety of glucosamine sources in a powder form to ensure that each of the benefits from the multiple ingredients is experienced. It includes MSM (methylsulfonylmethane) as an organic sulphur source to support glucosamine hydrochloride. It also includes glucosamine sulphate and supplies other cofactors needed for cartilage tissue or matrix synthesis. Younger animals with healthy antioxidant and chondrocyte-cell status can benefit from the glucosamine hydrochloride included in the formula; older animals will get good results thanks to the inclusion of glucosamine sulphate, which is better equipped to help overcome nitric-oxide interference. Chondroitin sulphate becomes a more important inclusion in joint regeneration and recovery formulas for older animals. The correctly engineered chondroitin molecule plays a central role in nitric oxide regulation in the chondrocyte. For the early cartilage damage and extra free-radical stress common in animal athletes a multi-ingredient formulation that addresses multiple requirements must be used. BioJOINT delivers this comprehensive strategy by supplying general antioxidant support, chondrocyte-specific antioxidants, cartilage building blocks, minerals, and vitamins, and it does so while maintaining the chondrocyte activity.

Osteo- and rheumatoid arthritis are generally at their worst in older animals and can be caused or accelerated by the presence of free radicals (which cause oxidation). Therefore additional antioxidants that enhance the effects of chondroitin are needed for nitric oxide and oxidation regulation. These additional antioxidants become important healing factors and tissue preservers for our aging animals. Antioxidants also have a role in the prevention and reversal of damage caused by rheumatoid arthritis.

Rheumatoid arthritis is different from osteoarthritis. Rheumatoid arthritis is an autoimmune condition, while osteoarthritis is a result of wear and tear or injury. The autoimmune condition eventually causes a massive immune system attack beyond the joint tissues. Because this illness is systemic, meaning it affects the whole body, symptoms of the autoimmune disease begin to appear in the organs, skin, and other tissues in due time. Antioxidants are critical for the maintenance and preservation of joint and other tissues regardless of the type of arthritis. (For a more comprehensive supply of antioxidants, use BioVITES to protect the body and enhance the effect of BioJOINT.)

Glucosamine hydrochloride is further supported if significant daily doses of vitamin C (1,000 to 3,000 mg per day) and grapeseed extract (proanthocyanidin) are part of the program. BioJOINT includes vitamin

C and grapeseed extract to provide this additional nutritional support. The standardized grapeseed extract (95 percent proanthocyanidins) provides a bounty of catechin, cyanidin, delphinidin, and other anthocyanins from the grape. It's worth noting that while grapes are known to be damaging to canine kidneys and can deliver a cumulative effect that is lethal, the pure grapeseed extract used in BiologicVET therapies does not contain the elements of grape that are harmful to our pets.

Other supportive herbs such as boswellia serrata extracts are included to further enhance anti-inflammatory activity. These elements can, among other things, block a chemical known as tumor necrosis factor (TNF), a signaling protein involved in inflammation. Boswellia serrata can be effective in the treatment of autoimmune disease such as rheumatoid arthritis.

Recovery of the joints, regardless of the type of arthritis, requires that the body be treated holistically. As previously described, this holistic or whole body restoration is important for recovery from any illness. This systemic retuning depends on improvement of gastrointestinal tract efficiency, immune system fine-tuning, and antioxidant saturation.

Therefore, despite the advantages of molecular size and targeted formulas, if the animal's intestinal health is inadequate, the product's effect will not be as powerful as it could be because these cartilage building blocks and cell activators will not be absorbed in high enough quantities. To ensure that this is not the case, BioJoint supplies digestive enzymes to improve nutrient digestion and absorption plus soluble and insoluble fibers to feed gut-friendly bacteria.

Gastrointestinal health is crucial to recovery from the symptoms of arthritis, and research confirms that this is especially the case when it comes to rheumatoid arthritis. Some experts believe that rheumatoid arthritis is caused by breaches in the gastrointestinal lining. Foreign particles infiltrating the circulation of the body trigger an immune system malfunction. BioJoint is designed to help improve the impermeable barrier in the gut lining.

BioJOINT PROFILE

INGREDIENT	ACTIVE ELEMENT	BENEFIT
Vitamin blend	Calcium ascorbate and ascorbic acid (vitamin C), vitamin D_3	crucial to joint maintenance, rebuilding, recovery and protection designed to support gene activity involved in bone mineralization
Mineral blend	Methylsulfonylmethane, manganese	important for cartilage restoration and maintenance provides immune system tools for better control of inflammation key minerals for bone integrity
Cartilage – glycosaminoglycan factors	Glucosamine sulphate potassium chloride, chondroitin sulphate, glucosamine hydrochloride	supplies building blocks for cartilage restoration provides nitric oxide regulation to activate the manufacture of glycosaminoglycan in the cells helps activate cartilage production at the genetic level while supplying the building blocks
Herbal support	Grapeseed extract, boswellia serrata	reduces levels of inflammatory prostaglandin hormones protects vitamin C so it is available for cartilage construction
Specific amino acids	L taurine, l glutamine, l cystine, l proline	improves insulin health supports anti inflammatory activity and glutathione antioxidant status to protect joint tissue provides immune system and lean muscle tissue fuels and nitrogen protects intestinal lining from detrimental effects of NSAIDS improves immune system (cytokine) efficiency critical amino acid for cartilage synthesis
Digestive enzymes	Bromelain	improves digestibility of nourishment to enhance bioavailability of food increases nutrient absorption and transport of joint building blocks also provides additional anti inflammatory activity improves feed efficiency
Food base carrier	Certified Organic Seed Blend (Flax, Sunflower, Sesame, Oat)	supplies key fatty acids, lignans, essential amino acids and fiber in a food format to maximize bioavailability food base supports delivery of the purified isolated vitamins and minerals also supplied in this product

EXTRA NUTRACEUTICAL HELP
FOR RHEUMATOID ARTHRITIS

Sometimes the immune system attack associated with rheumatoid arthritis is severe, and steroids are prescribed. A 2002 article in the *Journal of Leukocyte Biology* indicated that glucocorticoids (both natural and synthetic) stimulate the production of I-kappa-B, a cellular compound that ultimately blocks the chemistry that results in inflammation.

A 2001 Danish study reveals that S-adenosyl-methionine (SAMe), a common nutraceutical, has much the same activity as glucocorticoids although it works in a different way. While the steroids deal with the symptoms, SAMe can work to stimulate the synovial cells' production of synovial fluid, which fosters the recovery and reversal of the damage from rheumatoid arthritis. SAMe is powerful, and it doesn't deliver the sort of side effects corticosteroid therapy does.

SAMe is the perfect anti-rheumatoid compound to administer along with BioJOINT. It can be purchased in most health food stores. This ingredient cannot be mixed into the BioJOINT powder formula because it tends to gum up. It must be administered separately in pill form.

If your pet health-care practitioner is prescribing corticosteroids, you should ask that he or she look into SAMe as an alternative. Try it first, and if the powerful steroid must be applied after all, using SAMe and BioJOINT along with the steroid will reduce the amount of the steroid that's needed. As treatment progresses, the steroid dose can be slowly reduced and eliminated while SAMe and BioJOINT carry on with the job of managing the inflammation.

SAMe is not likely to be required for osteoarthritis because that form of arthritis is not a systemic condition. However, you may wish to consider using it because, in addition to the potent anti-inflammatory activity and regenerative support that SAMe offers, it also supports general metabolic health and is a great supplement for the treatment of depression. Many animals are in pain from joint disease and distressed by the loss of mobility, and they become anxious or depressed. SAMe can help your animal cope with the emotional upset that any form of arthritis may cause.

DIGESTIVE DISORDERS

In order for the body to extract the nutrient building blocks and essential nutrition from food, the gastrointestinal tract must be healthy. The benefits of any diet—healthy or otherwise—cannot be delivered if even mild gut insufficiencies hamper digestion and the absorption of nutrients. Poor gastrointestinal health can result in premature aging in younger animals and accelerated aging in older ones.

Anxiety due to separation, depression, excessive physical work, poor quality food, illness, injury, or the stress of surgery all interfere with digestion and nutrient availability. Poor mineral absorption can be caused by gastric acid deficiency and intestinal disease. Mineral deficiencies lead to hormonal inefficiencies and antioxidant impotence that in turn lead to illness that may never be linked to mineral deficiency. Gastrointestinal inefficiency will eventually result in multiple illnesses. And illness increases the demands for nutrients to aid recovery, setting up a digestive problem that can grow exponentially.

DIGESTIVE SUPPORT FROM THE BIOLOGICVET PROGRAM

The BiologicVET powders supply powerful and comprehensive gastrointestinal support, including a potent array of digestive enzymes, glutamine for intestinal tract lining integrity, and sulphur-containing antioxidants that protect the mucosal cells lining the intestinal tract. BioVITES, one of the foundation products, is designed with a little stronger support for digestion and optimal intestinal health. It delivers sufficient essential vitamins and minerals in the right proportions and in easy-to-absorb forms.

Chronic diarrhea is often quickly resolved with the addition of BioVITES to the dog's food. The potent digestive enzyme strategy in BioVITES contributes largely to the improvement. Severe cases of diarrhea may require added support from BioSKIN&COAT. This product provides potent antihistamine and anti-inflammatory activity that extends beyond just skin irritations to soothe inflammation in the gastrointestinal tract. If an undetermined allergen is causing the problem, BioSKIN&COAT can help block the negative response and end the problem.

General inflammation of the gastrointestinal tract in the form of colitis and inflammatory bowel syndrome are also functions of inflammation or related irritation. The bombardment of environmental toxins can produce gastrointestinal tract problems such as digestive impediments and inflammatory bowel problems. BioSKIN&COAT can be combined with BioFATS to help reduce and even eliminate inflammatory bowel syndrome and other intestinal problems.

In the case of stomach and intestinal disease, the challenge is one of compromised digestion and nutrient absorption. How does a body get what it needs for recovery of intestinal tissues when the digestive process is compromised? BioFATS is designed for easy absorption and fast action, supplying its own specialized enzyme system. Taken together, BioVITES and BioFATS provide powerful digestive and gastrointestinal support. If an even more potent therapy is needed to treat digestive allergies that are difficult to pinpoint, BioSKIN&COAT can be added to the program.

Consider a Diet for a Friendly Gut

Ensuring that a healthy diet makes up the majority of the food your dog eats will also help resolve many digestive problems. If problems occur frequently, a change in diet must be considered. High-glycemic carbohydrate sources may be hidden in feeds and contributing to the development of problems with fungi (yeast). Some animals are more vulnerable to negative effects from these feeds than others, simply because their immune systems are not able to regulate the fungus cultures. An animal that is able to tolerate the grain-loaded feed may simply have an immune system that keeps the fungi and pathogenic bacteria at bay.

If your dog appears to be vulnerable to damage from a grain-loaded diet, change to raw or freeze-dried feed that includes a healthy meat portion and excludes grains. Add BIOVITES to support healthy numbers of the helpful bacteria and prevent infiltration of opportunists with FOS fiber and other immune system support.

Basic gut-friendly bacteria are supported by fructo-oligosaccharide (FOS), a soluble fiber supplied in inulin. This is food for the gut bacteria, and supplementation is important because it is often missing from processed dog foods. FOS is a non-digestible fiber that can be sourced from artichoke/inulin. Fiber is crucial for intestinal health but not just any type will do. The BiologicVET formulations include both the soluble and insoluble fibers to provide a sustainable medium for the healthy bacteria, while providing healthy cleansing activity for the intestines. This support is welcome even in times of digestive calm and relative health and can strengthen the system for challenges to come.

FOS is known to produce a potent anti-inflammatory result in the cells lining the gastrointestinal tract. Research shows that probiotic administration produces the same anti-inflammatory effect that soluble fiber can to alleviate the inflammation associated with colitis and other IBDs. In other words, if the bacterial culture in the gut is healthy, these microbes can use the dietary fibre to produce an anti-inflammatory effect in the intestine.

Research is confirming how gut bacteria work and revealing the incredible health support these precious bacteria produce for the cardiovascular systems and brain health, plus powerful immune activity and insulin support. The short-chain fatty acids produced by the bacteria in the gut from these fibers enter the bloodstream and travel to the liver, heart, and brain to offer signals and fuels for these cells. Butyrate and proprionate are just a few of the fatty acids these specialized microbes produce and send on their way. These vital fats can even protect against cancers, including breast, endometrial, colon, and prostate. They also produce an easy-to-absorb source of B vitamins and vitamin K—essential nutrients for optimal health in humans and companion animals.

However, if the bacterial culture is depleted, adding the fiber may not deliver the results until supplementation with the live bacteria increases the intestine's microbial count. With a compromised bacterial culture in the intestine, our pets are vulnerable to pathogens that can cause rashes, dandruff, and dry skin. Yeast and other fungi travel very efficiently through the bloodstream to show up on the surface of the body as skin, nose, mouth, and ear infections. The fungi and bad bacteria can also lead to the development of urinary tract disease and infections around the genitals and anus. The missing friendly bacteria provide physical and biochemical obstructions to pathogens, including yeast infections. In extreme cases of microbe depletion, supplemental doses of the bacteria (probiotics) will help re-supply the intestine and build up the population faster.

RESTORING GUT-FRIENDLY BACTERIA

The gut-friendly bacteria of the gastrointestinal tract can make up 40-50 percent of immune system activity. Antibiotics, stress, poor quality feeds, chemical toxins, microbes, and more can obliterate this health supportive bacterial culture in a matter of days. Although many advocates of alternative medicine are passionately against the use of antibiotics, I don't know where we'd be without these marvels of medicine. It is true that they are overused, and this has resulted in the evolution of drug-resistant strains of microbes, or "superbugs." However, without antibiotics many common illnesses that are treatable today would otherwise result in mass death, as they did before the introduction of antibiotics.

To combat the ill-effects of antibiotic use or simply restore the good bacteria after a stressful time, gut-friendly bacteria (probiotics) must be re-introduced to the digestive system. Otherwise pathogens in the form of yeast, other fungi, or more dangerous invaders like *e.coli* or streptococci strains can infiltrate and weaken the immune system.

Restoration of these delicate gut-friendly bacteria can be accomplished by administering a variety of the Lactobacillus and bifidobacterium microorganisms at about fifty billion live organisms per day for two weeks. Products can range from 1 billion per capsule to 50 billion per capsule and more for the mixed blend. Read the label of the probiotic product carefully to determine the potency (live organism count). Keep in mind that the label shows a measure of the potency at manufacturing, so take into account the manufacturing date to establish a comfort level for the product's potency at the time of use. Also make sure that specific strains required for a dog's gastrointestinal tract are supplied, such as the *Lactobacillus reuteri*, *Lactobacillus acidophilus*, *Lactobacillus rhamnosus*, and *Bifidobacterium bifidus*. These strains will be detailed in the ingredient list.

Once the gut-friendly bacteria have been re-established, a month of maintenance dosing should follow. A daily treatment with a potency of five billion is sufficient to maintain your dog's healthy state after the two-week inoculation period. After at least six weeks of treatment, probiotic maintenance supplementation should be done one week a month as a precautionary measure, and this regular priming is especially necessary for seniors and animals with recurring ailments.

Although they do not supply the active organisms, each of the BiologicVET powders supports the proliferation and healthy status of existing gut microbes to strengthen the immune system and general metabolic health. These live organisms are not added to the powdered formulations because they could not survive in the mix of ingredients. In order to deliver health benefits, these probiotic organisms must be alive. Therefore, they must be supplemented separately. Any health food store and some pet supply stores will be able to supply these gut-friendly bacteria in the form of gel capsule supplementation or specialized yoghurt-like preparations.

OBESITY AND DIABETES

Beloved but inactive pets and pets that have been over-rewarded with food often gain weight—body fat—that puts unnecessary strain on their joints and organs and compromises their health and longevity. For many of the same reasons that humans become overfat and suffer health problems, pets can become obese. Humans commonly rate their body weight according to the BMI (Body Mass Index), although this method presents some degree of inaccuracy for athletes and some body types with lots of muscle. Measurements of lean body mass versus fat mass with bioimpedence devices or water displacement tanks provide more accurate measurements of fatness versus lean tissue. This applies to both humans and companion animals. However, when it comes to our pets, we can rely on a less scientific method, which can provide some pretty good guidance if we stay tuned in to their state of fitness on a day-to-day basis.

A fit dog will live longer, experience better life quality, and require less veterinary attention. Is your dog fit or fat? Fat accumulates throughout the dog's body but tends to collect around the neck and along the ribs and flank and underside. An animal with short hair should show a muscular neck and at least a hint of its ribs. The ribs tend to give more visible clues. If the ribs are covered completely by fat, your dog is likely crossing over to fatness, although rib appearance varies from breed to breed. Bulldogs, for example, tend to have a smoother appearance along the rib cage. Ask a breed specialist about fitness clues in your breed to set some benchmarks you can use, but keep in mind that weight standards even within any breed can vary drastically based on the different sizes and bone structure within the breed. The weigh scale is not a great measuring device; rib appearance is better.

Generally, an animal with a longer or coarser coat will hide the ribs but you should be able to feel them by probing with your fingers. If you cannot, your companion is at risk of over-fatness or obesity. Your pet should be physically fit to maximize health, happiness, and longevity. Feed intake can be varied based on activity level on a daily basis. Don't feed the same meal and volume day after day. I keep an eye on the fitness level of my animals, and, if they begin to look a bit softer or fatter, I back off on the feed volume for a few days until they assume a fitter appearance. The changes either way occur very quickly.

A more active animal requires more feed and on days when activity is greater, more food can be offered. If the ribs begin to show more on one day due to a few days of extra physical work, feed more food until a healthier *weight* is achieved. Better yet, feed a little more food in anticipation of the next day's physical work or immediately after a more physical day. For an obese animal, exercise can be painful and increase the risk of injury to joints. A sudden lunge by an overweight animal to fetch and play can cause cruciate ligament, cartilage, and tendon damage, requiring surgery and inflicting pain and emotional trauma. Obesity is usually accompanied by increasing insulin resistance, which can lead to inflammation and diabetes as well.

That said, insulin efficiency declines with age, even if the animal is not obese. Obesity just advances the insulin problem. We may have noticed that our own ability to recover from work or exercise has declined, and we can see that our companion animals don't recover from strenuous play as quickly after age seven or so. This is partly due to that decline in the efficiency of insulin that comes in the later years—the development of insulin resistance. If insulin efficiency can be maintained at youthful levels, the body operates more efficiently: nutrients are absorbed into cells more readily; protein synthesis for repair of tissues is more effective; the body's fat-burning furnaces remain active to help manage body fat; and inflammation is kept in check.

As insulin resistance progresses toward a diabetic state, the body tends to produce more pro-inflammatory hormones as a side effect. Ultimately, the cells become preloaded with pro-inflammatory hormones that can charge into action at the slightest provocation. General resistance to illness is lower in this pro-inflammatory state. Even before an outbreak of inflammatory disease, inflammation festers on a subclinical level. You may not see any symptoms in your pet, but there will be a daily impact that slowly erodes metabolic efficiencies and overall health. By the time diabetes is diagnosed, the inflammation and diabetes have been developing for some time.

There are two types of diabetes. The form often referred to as Type 1 diabetes is associated with a deficiency or complete shutdown of insulin production by the pancreas. Type 2 diabetes is associated with the cells' inability to use insulin to transport sugar from the blood. In Type 2 diabetes, the pancreas is producing insulin, but the receptor sites on cells are no longer sensitive to it and the sugar stays in the blood.

Many nutrients are now known to have gene-modulating activity, and the case of insulin-resistance-related diabetes in pets and humans is a perfect model for this nutragenomic influence. The BiologicVET program includes these nutrients in an effective and safe product that can help your pet slim down, become more active, and reverse insulin resistance and even diabetes.

BioSLIM

BioSLIM has been developed to target over-stuffed fat cells and the insulin-resistance that characterises pre-diabetes and diabetes. BioSLIM will improve the body's ability to burn fat away more efficiently with less physical effort. It also improves muscle tone and reactivates insulin efficiency. Not only does this formula trigger fat-burning activity (thermogenesis), it also blocks the absorption of those carbohydrate fillers commonly found in processed pet foods.

In addition to having specific ingredients that take advantage of the latest research into obesity and diabetes, all ingredients in BioSLIM are provided in doses that are appropriate, in line with the research, and able to deliver a physiological result. (Unfortunately, in order to keep costs down, many popular products on the shelves contain effective ingredients, but not in sufficient quantity. Essentially, their manufacturers are relying on the placebo effect to deliver results. This works to a limited degree in humans, but not at all in pets.) BioSLIM is made with the right proportion of the right ingredients. It is as powerful as a drug but without the side effects.

KEY INGREDIENTS

Vanadium sources such as vanadyl sulphate or bis (maltolato) oxo-vanadium have been shown to help regenerate glucose transport sites, reversing both Type 2 diabetes and pre-diabetes states of insulin resistance. The glucose transport sites are on the cell membrane surfaces and act as "doorways" into the cells. After activation by insulin, the sites pull blood sugar into the cells for metabolic processing. These glucose transport sites are the cell components that are desensitized to insulin's signal in the insulin-resistant state. Just like in us, our dogs have built-in genetic programs designed to constantly reproduce and replace these sites as they become damaged.

An animal (or a human) is considered to have diabetes when approximately 65 percent or more of these sites are damaged or blocked. Prediabetes states of insulin resistance, however, such as a 10, 20, or 50 percent loss of insulin activity result in proportional subpar metabolic health.

Multiple independent studies, like the one performed in 2002 at the University of British Columbia's Faculty of Pharmaceutical Sciences, demonstrate that vanadium sources can prompt the cells of the body to repair the damaged transport sites. This repair of the cell membranes, using the vanadium strategy, literally turns back the clock to rejuvenate a cell's communication systems. The cells are supposed to replace damaged transport sites on a perpetual basis, and this usually occurs efficiently in young animals and young humans. Aging tends to slow the genetic activity involved in the restoration process; which in turn ages the body faster.

Our pets might age relatively reliably until seven or ten years of age but after that the decline in general health is fast. If insulin resistance is in check, this acceleration of the aging process does not occur in the latter years; health is easier to manage. Obesity ultimately causes our pets to age faster since it promotes unhealthy levels of that subclinical inflammation and it contributes to the advancement of insulin resistance. Insulin resistance promotes obesity, and obesity further advances insulin resistance and therefore obesity—it's a self-perpetuating cycle.

If the progression of insulin resistance can be stopped, the risk of developing the many health challenges associated with it is reduced.

This includes diseases relating to the cardiovascular system, inflammation, and obesity, and histamine-related conditions. BioSLIM supplies forms of vanadium that deliver insulin support and ultimately help generate new cellular transport sites. It helps to reactivate genes responsible for reproducing new glucose transport sites that replace the old damaged ones. Doses of vanadyl sulphate in daily quantities of 1 mg per pound (2.2 mg/kg) of body weight deliver this regenerative result in companion animals. More on this breaking science is available at *http://www.biologicnr.com/2281*.

While both foundation products, BioFATS and BioVITES, support insulin efficiency, BioSLIM targets the insulin system with more precision and greater potency because it is designed to treat obesity and prevent the development of diabetes. The vanadium source in BioSLIM works best if it stays in both the gastrointestinal tract and the cells of the body in its reduced form. It therefore needs to be protected from oxidation, so specialized antioxidants accompany the vanadium source in the formulation. To that end, BioSLIM includes glutathione support and other antioxidants that facilitate vanadium's role. Here again, we see a multi-ingredient format supporting the transport and integrity of the biologically active compounds.

To physically reduce body fat, BioSLIM works at multiple levels to activate the fat-burning furnaces, primarily through safe thermogenic herbs. Brown adipose fat cells, whose function is to generate heat, can use fatty acids as fuel in their mitochondria. These cells burn dietary fat, turning it into heat. The thermogenic system can become less efficient or dormant with age. By re-activating the fat-burning system, body fat management will become easy. In order to maintain the activity of the thermogenic system, however, insulin resistance must be overcome because insulin resistance results in metabolic changes that also turn off thermogenesis. If the multiple systems are addressed simultaneously, the problem is treated long-term and metabolism corrected so obesity does not recur.

In addition to igniting the fat burners, BioSLIM also includes carbohydrate-blocking ingredients that reduce the digestion and absorption of carbohydrate. Corn is a common carbohydrate filler in pet foods, as are other common grains. These fillers contribute to poor insulin health and poor body fat management. The inulin fiber and white kidney bean powder in BioSLIM reduce the absorption potential of this unwanted carbohydrate and improve insulin's ability to regulate blood sugar to improve general health and metabolic rate. Some of our pets are more vulnerable to this carbohydrate load than others. BioSLIM comes to the rescue for those who have less tolerance to dietary carbohydrate and those who consume far too much of it in their daily meals.

If a lower calorie diet is combined with BioSLIM, the addition of BioVITES can ensure the diet is nutrient-dense and that the nutrients are bioavailable. In this case, BioSLIM and BioVITES could be used with a low-calorie diet to further enhance results without limiting nutrients. By maintaining the nutrient density of the diet, the body's natural health maintenance systems are supported even through periods when calories must be reduced.

Once insulin efficiency is re-established, your pet will experience better energy, strength, and endurance. He or she will recover from the daily walk or run more easily and with less stiffness. More body fat will be burned, and an improved metabolism will take care of long-term fat management.

BioSLIM PROFILE

INGREDIENT	ACTIVE ELEMENT	BENEFIT
Mineral blend	Vanadyl sulphate, chromium polynicotinate	improves insulin function jumpstarts gene systems involved in the restoration of insulin efficiency enhances sugar clearance from blood to insulin responsive cells improves and even corrects diabetic condition improved insulin health enhances fat management

Special activity	White kidney bean	improves gastrointestinal flora and management of dietary carbohydrate reduces absorption of insulin straining, fat contributing carbohydrate
Herbal support	Yerbe mate leaf powder, bitter orange extract, green tea extract, grapeseed extract, ginger root powder, bladder wrack	jumpstarts natural *fat burning* system (thermogenesis) improves thyroxin and thyroid efficiency
Specific amino acids	L glutamine, l taurine	improves function of insulin supports anti inflammatory activity and glutathione antioxidant status provides immune system and lean muscle tissue fuels and nitrogen retention in muscles
Digestive enzymes	Bromelain, papain, pancreatic lipase, protease	improves digestibility of nourishment increases nutrient absorption and feed efficiency
Food base carrier	Certified Organic Seed Blend (Flax, Sunflower, Sesame, Oat)	supplies key fatty acids, lignans, essential amino acids and fiber in a food format to maximize bioavailability food base supports delivery of the purified isolated vitamins and minerals also supplied in this product

Once your obese pet has lost some body fat, some regular exercise can be added to the program to improve energy levels and further speed weight loss. Start with the regular walk and as body weight continues to drop, increase the exercise to slow runs and then to faster, longer runs. As you work to increase your pet's fitness level, you will likely become healthier as well. Eventually you might be able to incorporate interval training to improve lean muscle tone, fat management, and longevity for the two of you.

If obesity and diabetes are long-standing conditions, you may need to continue to use BioSLIM. In most cases, however, once the target weight has been reached (and the necessary diet and lifestyle adjustments made to maintain the target weight), BioVITES and BioFATS will provide all the insulin support your pet's body needs.

Essential fatty acids, particularly docosahexaenoic acid (DHA) derived from marine oils, are powerful insulin support. Multiple studies, like the one performed by M.Taouis et al and reported in 2002 in the *American Journal of Physiology: Endocrinolgy and Metabolism*, confirm the powerful insulin-enhancing role of that polyunsaturated fat DHA.

BIOFATS is an excellent source of DHA. This is why the addition of BIOFATS and BIOSLIM to the feed daily can help reverse obesity even more effectively than BIOSLIM alone. BIOFATS, despite the name, will support metabolic health to improve fat-burning as well and should be continued after the need for BIOSLIM has melted away. Again, if feed volume is reduced in an effort to reduce calories, BIOVITES is also recommended as compensation to increase nutrient density of the diet. BIOFATS and BIOVITES together provide insurance that all the essential micro-nutrients are supplied sufficiently.

BEYOND INSULIN RESISTANCE

Minerals are critical to general hormone balance, and their status can decline significantly with age. Mineral deficiencies can be the root of age-related metabolic deterioration and what is perceived as general hormone resistance. Few health-care professionals identify mineral deficiencies as a cause of disease when their patients develop thyroid, adrenaline, testosterone, IGF-1, or dopamine anomalies. The common remedy for such problems is hormone therapy.

Copper, like chromium, zinc, and other minerals, is part of multiple metabolic activities. It figures in hemoglobin manufacture, connective-tissue synthesis, and bone-matrix construction. Copper is also involved in hormone production and regulation, in particular thyroid hormone, epinephrine, and dopamine. A lack of copper in the diet will result in insufficiencies related to these hormones, and hormone therapy will not fix the root problem.

BIOVITES is a rich supply of copper, zinc, and chromium. Sulphur is often destroyed during food processing, and MSM supplementation helps restore this important connective tissue building block. Sulphur plays a central role in the control of inflammation and hormone communication as well.

Amino acids can play a huge role in neurotransmitter and hormone health and receptivity as well. They can be used to prompt more efficient production of important hormones such as growth hormone. Exogenous hormone therapy should be the last resort, after alternatives, such as BioVITES, have been unsuccessful.

The more logical and least intrusive solution to hormone health is correction of the true cause—nutrient deficiency. Daily supplementation with active nutrition to maximize health potential and prevent the onset of hormone desensitization is often far more potent than drug therapy such as hormone replacement or hormone enhancement. It's also a more economical strategy than the regular veterinary visits that become more frequent as the years pass.

POOR COAT, HOT SPOTS, ITCHING, AND RASHES

Skin conditions in pets have become more and more common, likely a result of increasingly toxic surroundings. Our companion animals can experience high levels of skin diseases, including rashes, hot spots, and itching due to similar biochemical or biological systems that cause humans to experience symptoms of asthma. Just as skin disease in our pets has been on the rise, asthma in the human population is skyrocketing out of control. However, nutrition plays a huge role in the reactivity of allergens attacking from the surroundings. The trigger for an asthmatic or allergic response might be polluted air, mold, pollen, chemicals, dust mites, food protein, or dander, but the inability of the body to cope with the irritation can be caused by a biochemical predisposition that's set in the cells by fatty acid and other nutrient imbalances. Poor diet "hyper-sensitizes" cells to irritants and allergens. Historical exposure to irritants and the immune system activity triggered by that exposure play a role as well.

The hyper-sensitization of the body is ultimately a function of two things: an overload of the Omega-6 fatty acid known as arachidonic acid and an increased oxidation within the body. Just as diet can contribute to this two-pronged problem, diet can be changed to improve the fatty acid status and improve the antioxidant levels in the cells, reducing the dog's vulnerability to allergens. If you can tweak the diet to remedy the deficiencies, you should be able to "turn down" your dog's immune response to at least some of the substances in the environment, if not furnish its body with the ability to protect itself from these allergens altogether.

Regular doses of BioFATS can help re-establish the balance of the fatty-acid metabolism and reduce the severity of chronic inflammatory activity. Allergies are characterized by inflammatory activity that BioFATS can reduce on its own and even eliminate completely if the case is mild.

Research shows that inflammation increases histamine sensitivity and symptom development. BioFATS helps combat this excessive activity and as a consequence it works synergistically to further support BioSKIN&COAT. BioFATS reduces histamine response through a pathway that is different from the one used by BioSKIN&COAT.

BioVITES also works into this program by supplying antioxidant vitamins, minerals, and phytonutrients. These supplemented antioxidants combat elevated oxidation. Oxidation is known to accelerate production of the enzymes (known as COX enzymes) that convert the Omega-6 fatty acid (arachidonic acid) into inflammatory hormones. By increasing antioxidant status in the body with BioVITES, the rate at which inflammatory hormones are produced is reduced. Conventionally we resort to using COX-inhibitors such as NSAIDS (Nonsteroidal Antiinflammatory

Drugs) to combat inflammation. By using the BiologicVET Nutritional Foundation Program, BioFATS and BioVITES, general inflammation is better controlled.

BioSKIN&COAT

BioSKIN&COAT is a bioflavonoid-based antihistamine that naturally alleviates symptoms of allergies including those causing skin irritations, diarrhoea, congestion and wheezing. It's effective in the combat of seasonal allergies, food-borne allergies and even environmental allergens. It's also used successfully to help restore general coat health in cases where a specific cause may not have been pinpointed.

In the case of allergic reactions, diet-based corrective strategies don't normally provide immediate relief the way drugs can, so drug therapy like corticosteroid applications becomes the therapy of choice. We want fast results. However, drugs are not the only way to get fast results. Fast and powerful results are available without side effects of drugs. The combination of BioSKIN&COAT and BioFATS provides potent, reliable relief by combining antihistamine-like activity and anti-inflammatory activity.

Pruritis, for example, is common in our furry friends. This skin condition involves interaction of leukotriens, histamines, and prostaglandins that mediate the inflammation. It's a difficult condition to manage and sometimes the cause is never known. Drug therapy can work, but drugs can be required long-term for severe cases. BioSKIN&COAT is designed to help control these hormones. BioFATS supplies the building blocks to improve a balanced blend of these hormones as well. Most cases of pruritis can be completely resolved using BioSKIN&COAT and BioFATS concurrently. BioVITES is third on the list of priority for such cases. This is not intended to imply that BioVITES is not necessary, but this prioritization allows you to compound as many products as are affordable in a logical progression.

On the other hand, skin growths are not something to be immediately troubled about. If not benign and viral in nature, an alternative approach to surgery could work wonders. However, it is prudent to get a professional opinion as early as possible to determine the nature of the growth and ensure the growth does not advance to a dangerous size and stage.

Many of these surface growths are caused by viruses. Many growths that are associated with cancer are now known to be instigated by viruses as well. Skin cancer is a prevalent type of cancer in dogs and research indicates that excessive sun exposure will contribute to the problem in these cases, just as it does in humans. Research also indicates that a body saturated with antioxidants will also have a skin layer saturated with an antioxidant shield to work more powerfully than topically applied skin protection. BioVITES and BioSKIN&COAT deliver a healthy supply of these very antioxidants and other immune system fuels.

These nutritional factors provide potent protection from ultraviolet light and other chemicals that may cause lesions. Our pets' best defense against microbes, including viruses, is their own well-equipped immune system. However, if these viruses do get past the defenses to instigate surface growths, the most potent topical treatment we can apply is also a natural remedy. My favorite offensive attack when these virally induced growths develop is the application of oil of oregano at full strength. Oil of oregano, rubbed vigorously onto the growth two to three times daily will slowly but surely reduce the growth to a mere spot in just one week; in most cases it then just falls off. Be persistent and rub it in frequently. If the growth is virally induced, it will not survive!

Growths that are well under the skin and not on the surface are likely not to respond well to this strategy. Although, the oil has a mild transdermal potential, meaning it can penetrate through the skin, high enough concentrations may not reach the site, if any finds its way there at all. Prevention is better than a cure, and this involves limited sun exposure and potent antioxidant-rich nutrition. BioVITES and BioFATS daily provide potent protection. Adding BioSKIN&COAT further fortifies this protective sun and viral screen.

KEY INGREDIENTS

BioSKIN&COAT supplies a potent antihistamine activity that helps relieve irritated and inflamed skin caused by allergic reactions. Healthy doses of soluble fiber in this powder fuel the production of the valuable short-chained fatty acids by the gut-friendly bacteria that help the entire body, skin included.

BioSKIN&COAT can be used with BioFATS as a power-punch therapy where neither of these therapies used alone is enough to relieve the problem. BioFATS can supply the specialized Omega-3 fatty acids that the body might not be able to produce at levels needed to sustain healthy skin and coat. When these fatty-acid building blocks are available for balanced hormone production, hormone response to stimuli like potential allergens is balanced as well.

Most cases of skin disease respond well to this dual nutritional product approach to replace drugs. In fact, many animals require the use of corticosteroids to cope with allergic reactions because nothing else has worked. Some will have used these steroids for years. With the combination of BioFATS and BioSKIN&COAT, the problem can be treated, and the corticosteroids slowly tapered off and ultimately eliminated. Of course, such transitions must be made while monitored by the prescribing veterinary doctor or any other qualified medical professional willing to oversee the process. Every condition is different, just as each individual experiencing the illness is distinct.

Once the condition is eliminated or at least under control, the administration of BioSKIN&COAT can also be reduced in a tapered fashion to allow BioFATS to maintain the healed or controlled situation long-term. BioFATS should be used daily anyway to sustain healthy metabolic activity and powerful disease prevention.

Severe cases of skin disease might need the ongoing use of BioSKIN&COAT. Interestingly BioSKIN&COAT has been used successfully to treat cases of chronic diarrhea and vomiting in dogs. In these cases, it is delivering its therapeutic effects by circumventing a skewed autocrine hormone response in the layers of the gastrointestinal lining, preparing the cells to respond in a more balanced fashion—the same way it works on skin cells. In many circumstances, it is very difficult to identify an allergen; sometimes it's impossible to eliminate the trigger. BioSKIN&COAT can defuse the sensitivity in these cases.

Just like all the other powders of the BiologicVET series, the base of the BioSKIN&COAT formula includes a powerful array of digestive enzymes and immune system and cellular peptides. This tasty base is the source of the soluble fibers that feed the gut-friendly bacteria. All of these fundamental ingredients support biological correction so that long-term health can be maintained by the body.

Maintaining the colony of the gut-friendly bacteria is critical to overall health. The destruction of these organisms is often the underlying cause of illness, and this is too often the case when it comes to skin health. Ironically, antibiotics that are often used to treat these skin conditions also destroy the gut-friendly bacteria. BioSKIN&COAT addresses the microbe issue by fuelling the gut-friendly bacteria and stopping the infection cycle. BioSKIN&COAT also includes other key minerals such as sulphur and vitamins such as biotin, which are essential to this healing process. This ensures these nutrients are available abundantly to support long-term recovery. Read the labels carefully to find the dosing and the program that best suits your pet's needs. Some cases of skin disease will be harder to treat than others due to the environmental, dietary, and even genetic differences. This is why different levels of dosing and different combinations of the products will be needed to treat each distinct scenario.

BIOSKIN&COAT PROFILE

INGREDIENT	ACTIVE ELEMENTS	BENEFIT
Vitamin blend	Biotin	crucial to skin and coat maintenance, rebuilding, recovery and protection
Mineral blend	Methylsulfonlymethane, zinc,	important for skin and coat health and maintenance provides immune system tools for better inflammatory control and allergy management
Antihistamine activity	Quercetin dehydrate, biotin	delivers antihistamine relief relieves symptoms of allergies
Herbal support	Grapeseed extract	reduces levels of inflammatory prostaglandin hormones improves availability of antioxidant vitamin C increases peripheral blood to facilitate delivery of the natural histamine relieving agents to the skin
Specific amino acids	L glutamine, l cystine	improves insulin health so nutrients can be conveyed to tissues supports anti inflammatory activity and glutathione antioxidant status provides immune system and lean muscle tissue fuels and nitrogen protects intestinal lining from detrimental effects of NSAIDS improves immune system (cytokine) efficiency to help mitigate allergies
Digestive enzymes	Pancreatic lipase, papain, protease	improves digestibility of nourishment to enhance bioavailability of food increases nutrient absorption and transport of critical nutrients provides additional anti inflammatory activity
Food base carrier	Certified Organic Seed Blend (Flax, Sunflower, Sesame)	supplies key fatty acids, lignans, essential amino acids and fiber in a food format to maximize bioavailability food base supports delivery of the purified isolated vitamins and minerals also supplied in this product

FLEAS, TICKS, MOSQUITOES, AND MITES

Fleas, ticks, and mosquitoes are capable of causing a wide variety of illnesses and/or diseases, not just to pets but to their human companions as well. They are also a common cause of allergies and skin disease in our pets, as are mites. Ticks alone are the cause of approximately thirty major diseases, and there are also a number of illnesses and life-threatening diseases attributed to mosquitoes.

Unfortunately, many of the treatments designed to repel or eliminate these pests can be just as harmful and annoying as the diseases they cause. It will require some research on your part to determine the safety of many accepted treatments such as flea, tick, mite, or mosquito remedies. In fact, these pests can be repelled naturally. Fleas and mosquitoes are not as likely to infest animals whose blood is saturated with B-vitamins so supplementation can provide a mild blanket protection. My dogs, Lennox, Diesel and Dexter, have never required treatment with flea medications or baths.

Some of these conventional treatments contain organophosphate and organochlorine chemicals originally designed for chemical warfare to kill humans—nerve gas. They're used in many of our garden pesticides today as well. Small doses kill the pests but do not show immediate effects on the infested host animal. Small but frequent neurotoxin exposure can accumulate to impose significant consequences down the road including brain toxicity and cognitive disturbances. Organophosphates also interrupt the endocrine system to interfere with thyroid activity, pituitary function, and insulin efficiency (contributing to the development of diabetes). These compounds can also hamper sperm production, testosterone levels, and ovulation.

How much of this toxicity has your furry little family member already absorbed? How much more can be tolerated? Some can tolerate more than others but eventually the influence takes a toll. Read labels of food, drugs, and other treatments carefully.

AFTERWORD

YOUR PET'S HEALTH IS IN YOUR HANDS

It's not a coincidence that pets tend to be reflections of their human guardians on many levels. If we are conscious enough to recognize our pet's body language, we might be lucky enough to learn a lot about ourselves. If we are brave enough to accept the fact that their health challenges are in our control, we might be able to prevent illness in all family members. It is true—they tend to look and act a lot like us, and they tend to develop many of the health characteristics that the human family members may be vulnerable to, and for good reason.

If we lead an active lifestyle, we are more likely to choose upbeat companion animals that can inspire us and keep up with us. If we lead a life full of physical activity, the family dog will be right at our side, and, as a result, they will be as fit as we are. On the other hand, if we lead a sedentary life, our pets will be sedentary to accompany us. A sedentary lifestyle often leads to associated illnesses or health deficiencies found in both the human guardian and animal companion. Your companion may begin to experience these conditions before you do, which can serve as a warning of what may lie ahead for you. Change is in order for the entire family.

Pets also absorb the family stress. We may find that our family canine member is unsure showing signs of fear and uneasiness. Anger and emotional instability usually stem from insecurity. An unstable household breeds an insecure pet. Although other things factor into the emotional state of your family pet, such as interactions (or lack thereof) with its littermates and mother, as well as other experiences in life, our home environment will influence the predispositions to soothe or aggravate the situation. Physical illness can develop from the aggravation of emotional state.

Our dogs are much like a barometer of our own life, if we are honest enough to admit our vices and vulnerabilities. Our pets are highly sensitive to our emotional states; so much so that we may be able to gauge our own emotional health through their demeanour. Just think back to the last time you were on edge or carrying anger; your companion canine will have likely expressed some anxiety or uncertainty more spontaneously than your human family members or friends might have. Our pets play off our emotional states, reading postures and body language, literally smelling your state of emotions. They read human body language because this is a major form of communication amongst their canine community. Humans are less sensitive to these signs, but we still unconsciously express them. If you are aware of your animal's demeanour, you might learn more about how your attitude affects others in your life at a conscious and subconscious level.

In terms of a healthy environment, the family pet is our "'coalmine canary." The metabolisms of family cats and dogs run at a faster pace than our own. Therefore, any environmental toxins, nutrient insufficiencies, or social stressors we may share with them can manifest disease sooner in them than in our human family members. Heed the warnings and make changes for the entire family. The foods we choose for our pets will determine whether or not they are getting live nutrients that their bodies can use to keep disease at bay or allow illness to develop unchallenged. Don't take your pet's health for granted but just the same, ensure that you heed the broader message that their illnesses or lack thereof and emotional states may bring to light.

Of course, many illnesses are out of our control and may be a result of genetic predispositions, but even those can be mitigated if we employ preventive measures and natural remedies that correct the metabolic problem. A large dog like a Great Dane, for example, will be more vulnerable to hip degeneration than a Chihuahua might be. In addition, within the breed, the lineage might also have vulnerability that shows up in the animal's parents and litter mates. In cases where these joint diseases are common or likely, ensuring that the animal's diet supplies sufficient glucosamine, chondroitin, vitamin D, calcium, magnesium, and copper, can reduce the risk for premature development of the condition. Tissue-specific antioxidants that can jumpstart genetically driven health maintenance and recovery systems can also be applied to change the course of the genetic illness.

Your dog's health can be under your control just as your own health can be. An animal that is fit in mind and body is more resilient when coping with illness and is a happier, more harmonious member of the family. The addition of phytoantioxidants with general protective activity to the diet will help protect tissues and preserve healthy inflammatory regulation throughout the animal's life. Specialized polyunsaturated fats that are highly vulnerable to oxidation and rarely survive food processing are critical neurological building blocks that affect cognition factors and modify emotions.

Nutrition, a factor we dictate, will play a huge role in disease prevention and health management and this includes emotional state. We have control over health and disease by taking charge of the nourishment we and our pets eat and mitigating the unnecessary stress our lifestyles may be imposing. Today's nutraceutical research has allowed us to apply nutrient-based therapies with precision and potency as powerful as drug but without the side-effects. Apply these proven strategies to improve the life of your companion animals. Once you witness, for yourself, the formidable life change in your dependent pet, allow this epiphany to inspire change for the rest of the family. Your pet's health is in your hands. You now have the tools and know how to take charge.

APPENDIX 1
THE ESSENTIALS OF FATTY ACIDS

Essential fatty acids are one of the most commonly misunderstood categories of nutrition. Pet food and supplement manufacturers often send out unclear and occasionally blatantly incorrect information, confusing retailers and customers alike. These oils then land in the pet's food bowl, producing metabolic havoc instead of harmony. The right fat blend protects health and helps build long-term resistance to illness. The wrong ratios will slowly but surely contribute to illness. Supplementing with the wrong ratios of fatty acids for short periods may provide short-term benefits, but the long-term effect can be detrimental. Understanding the value and the concept of essential fatty acids is as critical to good pet health as it is to good human health.

There's no refuting it. Omega-3 fat supplements, such as EPA and DHA derived from cold-water fish, deliver the building blocks for healthy cell membrane structure, vigorous receptor site status, and good hormone balance. These fatty acids are essential for good health; they're essential for life, and they are often called "essential" because the body can be faced with a condition whereby it cannot make them. But they are not really essential fatty acids by the definition of the term 'Essential Fatty Acid'. They are named more appropriately 'Conditionally Essential Fatty Acids'. If the cells are faced with nutrient deprivation, a genetic anomaly, or a sluggish metabolism, the cells cannot produce these fatty acids at an acceptable rate even if the essential fat, linoleic acid were to be supplied abundantly by the diet. If these conditions slow the cell's natural process

down, EPA and DHA must be supplemented to make up for the shortfall—conditionally essential. (refer to the fatty acid flowchart diagram)

We expect the cells of the human body and those of cats' and dogs' to manufacture the longer-chain, nonessential fatty acids like DHA (docosahexaenoic acid) and EPA (eicosapentaenoic acid) from the short-chain, essential fatty acids that food has provided. In the dog and cat, the Omega-6 linoleic acid is converted into the Omega-3 linolenic acid which is then used to make the Omega-3 DHA and EPA. Following these conversions in the flowchart provided allows for a better understanding. Humans cannot convert the linoleic (Omega-6) into linolenic (Omega-3) like cats and dogs can. For humans linoleic (Omega-6) and alpha linolenic (Omega-3) acids must be supplied by the diet – they are both essential in the classic definition of the term. For dogs, linoleic (Omega-6) acid is the only essential fatty acid which must be supplied by the diet. Cats are different again whereby two Omega-6 fatty acids are essential – linoleic acid and arachidonic acid.

In all these species the DHA and EPA Omega-3 fatty acids (which can be supplied abundantly by cold water fish oils) are nonessential but can be required as conditionally essential if the essential fats or metabolic efficiencies are limited. However, treatment of a condition with fish oils to administer DHA and EPA without considering a supply of the essential fatty acid doesn't make sense at all. We must also supply the essential fatty acid which the body needs to make the very DHA and EPA we are supplementing so it is equipped with the building block to catch up with DHA and EPA production on its own. It also needs this base nutrient for other metabolic and structural functions. Again, in dogs and cats this essential is the Omega-6 linoleic acid while humans need both the Omega-6, linoleic acid, and the Omega-3, alpha linolenic acid.

When we supplement with these fatty acids we are influencing the body's production of specialized hormones by altering the proportion of these fatty acids in the diet. Ultimately we are changing the production proportions of hormones called prostaglandins (PGE) or eicosanoid hormones of which there are many and different classes. The classification of these hormones relies, in part, on the fatty acid source. Again, the accompanying flowchart represents the conversion path of these essential fatty acids providing a visual snapshot of this process. If we or our animals lack the Omega-3 fatty acids a tendency or predisposition for inflammation can occur due to a relative overload of PGE2 which advances inflammation.

However, if we blast the body with Omega-3 supplementation from fish oils to promote the PGE3 production shown in the flowchart we can help neutralize inflammation through better balance between the inflammatory PGE2 and the relatively anti-inflammatory PGE3. This balance is created through two mechanisms: one is the greater availability of the PGE3 precursor to make more PGE3 and the other related mechanism is the use of enzymes for this Omega-3 conversion which makes the same enzymes unavailable for the conversion (desaturation) of the Omega-6 fats into those inflammatory prostaglandins (PGE2). As a result of this activity more PGE1 is produced from the essential linoleic acid instead of more PGE2 accumulating from the same building block.

Balanced supplementation blocks excessive PGE2 (inflammatory prostaglandins) production while producing more of the relatively anti-inflammatory prostaglandins.

However, if the Omega-6 fat, linoleic acid is not concurrently supplied we can create an imbalance in the other direction limiting PGE1 production. PGE1, derived from linoleic acid, has profoundly important roles and its limitation can result in metabolic problems. To name a few roles, it's involved in nerve impulse propagation, neurotransmitter conveyance, intestinal health and smooth muscle activity. Fish oils will not supply sufficient quantities of the essential Omega-6, linoleic acid. The two classes of fatty acids must be supplemented at the same time in order for the production flow of these two hormone classes to ensue at a balanced rate due to the enzyme influence each class—Omega-3 and Omega-6- has on the other. Together these different classes of hormones produce harmony in the body. If one of these two classes of fatty acids is off balance or missing in the diet, the cells will produce an imbalanced hormone status.

Fatty Acids are Rarely Supplied by Food

At the root of this fatty acid dilemma is the processing of food which destroys these essential fats due to the high heat and extensive oxygen exposure. This heat and oxygen exposure also destroys the natural antioxidant levels in the food stripping the food of the elements which protect the fats naturally and preserve the genetic activity within the cells designed to use these fats. As described in Appendix 2, Oxidation 101, oxidation accelerates the genetic activity responsible for COX activity advancing the conversion of Omega-6 fatty acids to hormones which have inflammatory activity. Exaggerated inflammatory activity is a function of multiple misaligned forces; an imbalanced Omega-3 to Omega-6 fatty acid status in the cells forming a state which is preloaded for inflammation; and another is elevated oxidation in the absence of proportionally opposing antioxidant activity which unnaturally accelerates the genes responsible for converting this preloaded status into inflammatory hormones. These adverse forces can be advanced by processed foods and poor diet.

Analysis of a food supply may indicate that these foods have abundant and even excessive amounts of the Omega-6 linoleic acid to meet essential fatty acid needs. Maybe so, but processing and storage of the food eventually damages the delicate structure even though the Omega-6 category (more stable molecule) of the fatty acids can tolerate processing a little better than the Omega-3 fatty acid can. Supplementation must address each level of the metabolic need in order to completely solve the limitations, antioxidant intake included. Fatty acid health in the body also depends on key vitamins and minerals which can also be compromised in processed food. These micronutrient cofactors often make up important components of enzymes involved in the cellular metabolism of fatty acids and other macronutrients

Research conducted to evaluate the two categories of fatty acids in dogs—Omega-3 and Omega-6—proves they are both needed concurrently in supplementation regimes despite the base food source. Presence of the Omega-6 linoleic acid limits enzyme activity on the Omega-3 side of the flowchart. This Omega-6 fatty acid load uses up the enzymes needed by the Omega-3 fatty acids for desaturation from alpha linoleic acid to DHA and EPA. The same is true in reverse whereby the Omega-3 DHA and EPA tie up the same desaturase enzymes to ensure that Omega-6 conversion to the inflammatory hormones is moderated.

One study showed that the health improvements resulting from supplementation with the Omega-3 DHA and/or EPA can slowly revert back in time to the diseased state. This is often what consumers report anecdotally as well. While supplementation of the study group using the Omega-6 linoleic acid had a slower onset of results they were sustained long term beyond the point that reversion took place with the Omega-3-exclusive group. There is a need to improve a health condition with immediate correction of the imbalance using the Omega-3 fatty acids such as those from fish oils. However, according to these findings we must also give the dog's cells the root building block fatty acid—the true essential Omega-6 fat, linoleic acid—in a biologically live form which has not been damaged by food processing so it can be used to restore self-sufficiency. The key to long term health is self-sufficiency.

Aging and Essential Fatty Acids

An aging metabolism can result in slower production of the Omega-3 DHA and EPA fatty acids in the tired cells as well; another condition which leads to the DHA and EPA fatty acids being Conditionally Essential as supplements. In fact, studies show that neuromembrane DHA levels can decline significantly with age contributing to neurological impediments as basic as memory loss to clinical illnesses like schizophrenia. Lack of DHA in the brain cells has also been linked to temperament impediments and even aggression. Brain tumors are found to have much lower DHA levels than normal brain tissue. An age-related decline in antioxidant levels in the cells can damage omega-3 fatty acids to alter status. Since the highly unsaturated EPA and DHA are more vulnerable to oxidation than even the base essential linoleic and alpha linolenic fatty acids, a lack of antioxidants allows them to be destroyed by cell-borne free radicals. Thus we require antioxidant and DHA and EPA supplementation in higher concentrations as we age.

In addition to having the right amount of the right kind of fats, the fatty acid supplements must be supplied in the right *proportion* or ratio with other supporting nutrients to ensure that the desaturase enzyme activity is moderated. Salmon oil must be combined with plant seed oils in the right combinations to meet the specific ratios of Omega-3 to Omega-6 fatty acids that dogs need. This gets them that root building block essential fatty acid, linoleic acid. Salmon oil alone does not supply relevant amounts of the Omega-6 essential fatty acid, linoleic acid. Additionally, the support nutrients which themselves are Essential Nutrition, such as vitamins, minerals and protective antioxidants should be supplied concurrently. If the dietary choices or the digestive process has contributed to fatty acid limitations in the body it is also likely that these limitations have contributed to other nutrient deficiencies which should be addressed in the form of general vitamin, mineral and amino acid supplementation. A comprehensive blend of vitamins, minerals, and phytoantioxidants can be supplemented daily with the fatty acid supplement to fulfill this need completely and maximize the cells` ability to handle these fatty acids in the appropriate way.

Your Dog Needs a Precise Fatty Acid Profile
Your dog needs a precise ratio of Omega-6 to Omega-3 fats to produce a precise hormonal cascade. A very important fact to keep in mind is the species-specific needs of essential fatty acids. Too many products in the pet sections of stores today are relabeled products which were originally designed for human use.

After all, if it's good enough for you and me, it should be good enough for Fido. Not true. I cannot highlight enough that the essential nutrient needs for our canine companions are quite different from our own and the fatty acid category of nutrition is one that differs immensely. Again, you and I need the diet to supply the essential fatty acids linoleic acid (Omega-6) and alpha linolenic acid (Omega-3) as the chart on the next page outlines. From these essentials our cells should be able to produce the downstream compounds although we can benefit from some additional DHA and EPA supplementation due to common metabolic hiccups which often lead to limitation. The chart demonstrates the additional conversion your canine companion is capable of, changing how and what is required by those cells. Choose a fatty acid supplement designed specifically for your dog's or cat's metabolism and make sure it's a proper blend of seed oils with cold water fish oils.

References:
(1) Franco Cavaleri; Potential Within A guide to Nutritional Empowerment: P 251-287; copyright 2003
(2) Gurleyik E, Coskun O, Ustundag N, Ozturk E; Prostaglandin E1 maintains structural integrity of intestinal mucosa and prevents bacteria translocation during experimental obstructive jaundice. Department of Surgery, Abant Izzet baysal university, Duzce Medical Faculty, Duzce Turkey; J Invest Surg 2006 Sept-Oct; 19 (5) :283-9
(3) Eguchi S, Kawano T, Yinhua, Tanaka K, YasuiS, Mawatari K, Takahashi A, Nakaya Y, Oshita S, Nakajo N.; Effects of PGE1 on vascular ATP-sensitive potassium channels.; Department of Dental Anesthesiology, Tokushima University School of Dentistry, Tokushima Japan; J Cardiovascular Pharmacology, 2007 Dec; 50(6):686-91
(4) Yasutoshi Itoh, Tadashi Yasui, Hiroaki Kakizawa, Masaki Makino, Kentaro

Fujiwara, Taiya Kato, Shigeo Imamura, Keiko Yamamoto; et al; The therapeutic effect of Lipo PGE1 on diabetic neuropathy-changes in endothelin and various angiopathic factors Department of Internal Medicine, Fujita Health University School of Medicine, Toyoake, Aichi 470-1192, Japan; accepted 13 June 2001

(5) D.F. Horrobin, "The relationship between schizophrenia and essential fatty acid and eicosanoids metabolism," Prostaglandins, Leukotrienes and Essential Fatty Acids 46.1(1992):71-77.

(6) John K Maesaka, Thomas Palaia, Linda Frese, Steven Fishbane and Louis Ragolia Prostaglandin D2 synthase induces apoptosis in pig kidney LLC-PK1 cells: Kidney International (2001) 60, 1692-1698; doi:10.1046/j.1523-1755.2001.00989.

(7) R P Kaufman, Jr, H Anner, L Kobzik, C R Valeri, D Shepro, and H B Hechtman Vasodilator prostaglandins (PG) prevent renal damage after ischemia. Ann Surg. 1987 February; 205(2): 195-198.

(8) Re S, Zonaletti M, Emanuele E. Aggressive dogs are characterized by low Omega-3polyunsaturated fatty acid status. Vet res Community, 2008 Mar:32(3):225-30.Wpub 2007 Sept 19

(9) Mayser P, Mayer K, Mahloudjian M, Benzing S, Kramer HJ, Schill WB, Seeger W, Grimminger F.; A double-blind, randomized, placebo-controlled trial of n-3 versus n-6 fatty acids-based lipid fusion in atopic dermatitis; JPEN J Parenter Enteral Nutr, 2002 May-June; 26(3):151-8; Department of Dermatology and Andrology, Justus-Liebig-University, Giessen, Germany;

(10) Shiro Urano et al, "Aging and oxidative stress in neurodegeneration," BioFactors 7.1-2(1998):103-112

(11) Saevik BK, Bergvall K, Holm BR, Saijonmaa-Koulumies LE, Hedammar A, Larsen S, Kritensen F; A radnomized, controlled study to evaluate the steroid sparing effect of essential fatty acid supplementation in the treatment of canine atopic dermatitis; Vet Dermatol. 2004

Jun:15(3):137-45; Department of small Clinic Sciences

(12) Berbett AA, Kondo CR, Almendra CL, Matsuo T, Dichi I; Supplementation with fish oil and olive oil in patients with rheumatoid arthritis.; Department of Pathology, Londrina State University, Parana, Brazil; Nutrition 2005 Feb; 21(2):131-6

(13) Kremer JM, Lawrence DA, Jubiz W, DiGiacomo R, Rynes R, Bartholomew LE, Sherman M.; Dietary fish oils and olive oil supplementation in patients with rheumatoid arthritis. Clinical and immunological effects. Department of medicine, Albany Medical College, NY 122208; Arthritis Rheum, 1990 Jun; 33(6):810-20

Flow chart of essential fatty acid processing by the cells in Dog, Cat and Man to make eicosanoid hormones. Linoleic acid is the only true essential fatty acid in Dogs. Linoleic and Arachidonic Acids are both essential in Cats. Linoleic and Alpha Linolenic Acids are the only essential fatty acids in man.

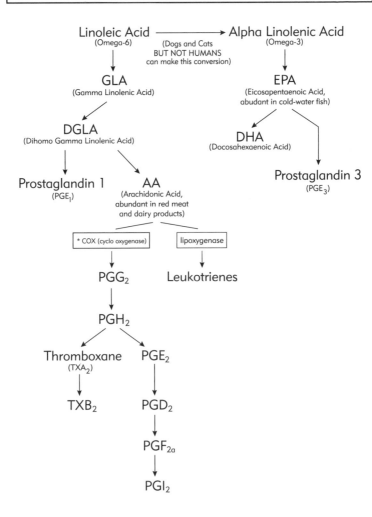

APPENDIX ESSAY
OXIDATION 101

The free radical is much more than just "a bad chemical that inflicts damage," and there's a lot more to the antioxidant than its "good-guy image". In fact, our cells and the cells of our companion animals rely on free-radical activity for many life-supportive processes such as immune function and oxidation of nourishment for energy production within the cells. The free radical only becomes a liability in the body when the cells fail to control its activity or reactivity. Antioxidants help control free radicals.

Since they support the immune system and protect tissues, antioxidants have a "good-guy" image. However, an antioxidant can become dangerously reactive in the body and may impart free-radical activity itself under certain conditions. The adverse activity of the antioxidant is more likely to occur if an antioxidant system is incomplete. A cell that fails to produce its requisite antioxidant levels on its own will face the uncontrolled fire of unbridled free radicals. The antioxidant from oral supplementation can come to the rescue.

The body can manufacture antioxidants to protect itself from intruding chemicals and even normal by-products of metabolism, including free radicals. This production can vary from individual to individual and, in part, this variance is responsible for the differing levels of tolerance to disease we all exhibit. Internal production of protective enzyme/antioxidants such as catalase, superoxide dismutase and glutathione peroxidase, depends on a genetic factor as well as the supply of integral nutrients such as copper, sulphur, selenium and manganese,

to name a few. Processed foods tend to be deficient in these important minerals. As we and our pets age, however, this endogenous (internal) production can decline as well.

Vitamins like C, E, alpha lipoic acid and even D can be supplemented to help offset this decline. Phytoantioxidants such as grapeseed extract, boswellia serrata and curcumin can also be added to the oral mix to improve antioxidant status in the body and help neutralize free radicals which have broken away from a controlled system and have become unbridled. However, poor antioxidant formulations can fuel the free radical fire.

Essential for biological health, free radicals are both facilitators and inhibitors of various biochemical systems, including hormone regulation; nitric oxide and peroxynitrite, the nitric-oxide-derived free radical, are good examples. In some cases free radicals promote tumor growth, but in other instances they fight tumor progression. Furthermore, free radicals are now recognized as gene modulators, a finding that differs immensely from the previous understanding that they exclusively mutate genes.

The answer to this complex biological riddle is to know the functions of the different types of free radicals and identify the triggers that may turn helpful ones against us and our companion animals. If you're able to gain a genuine appreciation for the interactions and influences that our foods and the nutrients they contain have on our biochemistry, you're more likely to take the recommendations in this book more seriously and apply them as long-term lifestyle commitments.

These intricacies are incorporated right into the formulation recommendations.

Various chemicals, those of unnatural origin as well as many that are natural by-products, can instigate and proliferate free-radical generation to increase the risk of disease. In other words, no matter how hard we try we can't escape the free-radical assault from our environment. This activity strikes right through us and our companion animals like lightning.

Free radicals don't just bounce off skin as though it were a metal shield and the free radical a rubber bead. The free radical that's generated outside the body can, upon contact, damage the molecules or atoms that make up skin. The reactivity doesn't end there. It continues like a domino effect through the skin to affect molecules in contact and close proximity—an indefinite chain of reactivity.

Protection from this hazard comes in the form of cell-incorporated antioxidants such as vitamin E and alpha lipoic acid, which slow down the reactivity. The antioxidant shield acts more like a sponge or a goopy gel matrix to absorb the momentum of the free radical that ricochets our way. With this gel matrix in place the free radical can't filter through as quickly or as deeply.

However, the absorption potential of antioxidants is limited, so that the more toxicity we or our pets are exposed to, the more light from the sun, the more oxidized food they eat, the more household cleaners, the more stress and food-borne poisons, the more absorption potential is needed in the form of the antioxidant.

Keep in mind that once the body runs out of absorption potential, the ultraviolet-light, toxin-activated and stress initialized free radicals are allowed to infiltrate deeper into the body where, if your pets' cells are prepared, they'll meet a second line of antioxidant defence guarding the core. If the body is not properly fortified, though, free radicals will invade further, literally scalding the delicate body from the inside out and altering the inbuilt genetic activity.

Compounding this bombardment from the outside, the body produces free radicals by way of metabolic activity. Emotional and mental states drive free-radical generation, as well. In addition, free radicals and other toxins are also taken inward through air and food. A larger intake of calories results in greater metabolic activity and more free-radical production at the body's core. With more physical activity, more oxygen is metabolized, and this, as well, increases the rate of cellular free-radical generation. Frankly there's no escape. Free radicals will flood the body from the outside in and the inside out.

Antioxidant protection must be supplied completely to protect the body from uncontrolled combustion. An effective program is much more than singular antioxidants; it's complex and comprehensive.

FREE-RADICAL GENERATION

Often a chemical reaction in the body doesn't proceed as cleanly as it should. Extreme demands from intense physical exercise and disease, as well as the influence from environmental chemicals, metabolic by-products, and dietary and stored nutrient supplies, influence how efficiently reactions ensue in the cells.

The reaction can also yield atoms with an odd number of electrons in the outer orbits, leaving behind an unpaired electron. To state it in simple terms, atoms are more stable when electrons on the outer most orbit of the atom are paired. Essentially an atom with an odd-number of electrons in the outer orbital isn't positive, negative, or neutral in terms of *electrical* charge. In fact, it isn't even considered an ion; it's a free radical, an unstable atom or molecule with an unpaired electron in search of a companion electron.

Free radicals formed from oxygen are nasty substances called a superoxide anion radical, O^{2-e}. They can also form a hydroxyl radical, HO^{-e}. Both are extraordinarily vicious and quite common. The unstable free radical requires an electron to offset the imbalance that this odd electron number imposes. It can suck an electron from another atom that makes up part of a molecule in the cells or vital chemicals of the body. When an electron is ripped away from an atom that's part of vital tissue, the atomic structure of this tissue's atom is altered and so are its chemical properties.

Ultimately this affected molecule and the tissue it constitutes are damaged. The free radical can tear away an electron from an atom of a molecule that exists in the genetic code of DNA. The result is a mutated code that can subsequently impair cell function. This process can instigate disease if the immune system or the natural DNA-corrective chemistry isn't able to discard or fix the mutation. Such a radical reaction isn't isolated to a single event, either. It's not slow and certainly not finite. It's more like a flash that rips through the body with lightning speed. The sacrificed molecule that neutralizes the original free radical, whether antioxidant or not, doesn't terminate the reaction. The sacrificed atom has one less electron in its outer orbit and is now a free radical itself. A wide variety of free radicals have affinities for different molecules and tissues and one antioxidant might have a greater capacity to neutralize one type of free radical and not another.

Chatecholamines like dopamine and epinephrine (adrenaline) are highly reactive and initiate the production of free radicals as does hydrocortisone. While moderate chate-cholamine secretions can protect the body by delivering antioxidant protection, oversecretion is oxidative, promoting free-radical generation. Prolonged periods of stress can result in incremental levels of epinephrine and corticosteroids that ultimately give rise to greater levels of free radicals. This is one way emotional and mental strains increase oxidative stress on the body and heighten the risk of disease. The stress-produced superoxide anion radical is a dangerous piranha that chews away at the body.

Unregulated serum glucose breeds free radicals, as well. As we've seen in previous chapters, glucose can react detrimentally with long-lived body proteins such as cartilage and other vital proteins to produce an advanced glycosylated end product (AGE)—a damaged protein. Free radicals play a facilitative role in this reaction.

If these free radicals are allowed to chip away at the body's antioxidant stores such as glutathione and vitamins A, C, and E, to name just a few, disease is inevitable. This degeneration of antioxidant protection results in an increased risk of cardiovascular ailments and chronic inflammation, diabetes and more.

ENTER THE ANTIOXIDANT

Antioxidants such as vitamins C and E, catechins, flavonoids, and polyphenols of plant origin supply the electrons required to neutralize free radicals so that the latter don't steal electrons from the atoms that make up vital molecules, cells, and tissues. However, that's not the only activity of these powerful biomodulators.

An antioxidant readily gives up an electron to neutralize the reactive free radical, but it's left with an unpaired electron that can also become a free radical. Antioxidants work in synergistic combinations. One type, such as vitamin E, can't replace the function of another, say, vitamin C or grapeseed extract and vice versa. The claims that grapeseed extract is so much more powerful than vitamin E aren't completely true. The wide array of free radicals requires a varied arsenal of specialized antioxidants. Vitamin E, for example, isn't able to neutralize all of the free radicals that glutathione or grapeseed extract can, but glutathione or grape seed can't effectively counteract all of those that vitamin E can.

There may be overlap in the potential of antioxidants, but there definitely isn't complete redundancy. In addition, antioxidants actually rely on one another for interaction to complete their roles. When an antioxidant becomes a free radical, it relies on its antioxidant partner to supply it with an electron to bring it down from its reactive state. The second donor, however, becomes a free radical itself, having given up its electron, so it requires a donor of its own. Each time this co-dependent reaction takes place the free-radical reaction potential (oxidative potential or reactivity level) drops to a lower level and becomes less risky to the body. Complete antioxidant programs are crucial to the total diffusion of this destructive activity.

By limiting the availability of these antioxidants in the body, completely or in part, we become vulnerable to the original reactive free radical at the top of the chain or any of the free radicals that are left in a reactive state at the point where the co-dependent antioxidant is missing from the chain. It's easy to induce a toxic outcome with a megadose administration of vitamin E, for example, and this is exactly what unaware scientists do when they show negative effects with supplementation of antioxidants. Typically toxicity assessments are done with extremely high megadoses of incomplete antioxidant systems. Antioxidants only work in systems made up of co-dependent antioxidant partners.

Some experts report irresponsibly that these life supporters can be toxic. I can assure you that if you eliminate these nutrients from your diet while wading through today's cesspool, free radicals will eat you and your pet alive. Today's epidemics are proof of this environmental danger. Supplement with antioxidants correctly and free radicals won't be able to sink their teeth into your armor. In order for this protection to be effective, however, a complete antioxidant plan must be employed.

These antioxidants also protect the activity of genes and not just the integrity of gene structure. Oxidation is now shown to literally accelerate the activity of genes. One such example is that of COX (cyclo-oxygenase), an enzyme responsible for the synthesis of inflammatory hormones. Oxidation accelerates this conversion to increase the level of inflammatory prostaglandin (PGE2) hormones beyond healthy levels. Typically we use COX inhibitors like nonsteroidal anti-inflammatory drugs (NSAIDS) to block the enzyme. We can also administer target specific antioxidants which block the unnaturally elevated level of oxidation so the gene can function according to its natural design. In this case, the downstream activity of the COX inhibitor (NSAID) will not be required long term.

Antioxidants can be critical navigators of hormone production by the cells from essential fatty acids. Therefore polyunsaturated fatty acid supplements must be used in conjunction with appropriately formulated antioxidant systems as natural metabolic guides for the fats. Gene modulation by nutrient-based compound is also a reality in the treatment of diabetes, obesity and chronic inflammation. Research is also demonstrating similar activity at the level of the chondrocyte, the cartilage cell responsible for using glucosamine to manufacture collagen in the joint tissue. These cells can become slow and even dormant in the face of oxidation which converts their nitric oxide levels against them; into the inflammatory peroxynitrite free radical.

The right antioxidant blends can neutralize the variety of imposing free radicals to allow the genes to work according to design- health restoration and maintenance. Since the cells of the aging body begin to slow down their production of endogenous (internally pro-duced) antioxidants oral supplementation must be administered to compensate and maintain youthful function of the body. Antioxidants preserve the integrity of the genetic codes, their downstream messenger molecules and the cells and networks of the intricate biological system.

References:

(1) P. S. Wong et al., "Inactivation of Glutathione S-Transferases by Nitric-Oxide-Derived Oxidants: Exploring a Role for Tyrosine Nitration," *Archives of Biochemistry and Biophysics* 394.2 (2001): 216–28.

(2) Ricardo Gredilla et al., "Effect of Short-Term Caloric Restriction on H_2O_2 Production and Oxidative DNA Damage in Rat-Liver Mitochondria and Location of the Free-Radical Source," *Journal of Bioenergetics and Biomembranes* 33.4 (2001): 279–87.

(3) W. J. Durham and M. B. Reid, "Generation of Reactive Oxygen and Nitrogen Species in Contracting Skeletal Muscle: Potential Impact on Aging," *Annals of the New York Academy of Sciences* 959 (2002): 108–116.

(4) J. S. Noh et al., "Neurotoxic and Neuroprotective Actions of Catecholamines in Cortical Neurons," *Experimental Neurology* 159.1 (1999): 217–24.

(5) T. G. Hastings and M. J. LaVoie, "Dopamine Quinone Formation and Protein Modification Associated with the Striatal Neurotoxicity of Methamphetamine: Evidence Against a Role for Extracellular Dopamine," *Journal of Neuroscience* 19.4 (1999): 1484–91.

(6) P. Dandona et al., "Effect of Hydrocortisone on Oxygen Free-Radical Generation by Mononuclear Cells," *Metabolism: Clinical and Experimental* 47.7 (1998): 788–91.

(7) J. Gasic-Milenkovic et al., "Protein 'AGEing'—Cytotoxicity of a Glycated Protein Increases with Its Degree of AGE Modification," *Zeitschrift für Gerontologie und Geriatrie* 34.6 (2001): 457–60.

(8) S. Gupta et al., "Hyperglycemia Increases Endothelial Superoxide That Impairs Smooth Muscle Cell Na+-K+-ATPase Activity," *American Journal of Physiology: Cell Physiology* 282.3 (2002): C560–66.

(9) T. Inoguchi et al., "High Glucose Level and Free Fatty Acid Stimulate Reactive Oxygen Species Production Through Protein-Kinase-C-Dependent Activation of NAD(P)H Oxidase in Cultured Vascular Cells," *Diabetes* 49.11 (2000): 1939–45.

(10) Priya Mohanty et al., "Glucose Challenge Stimulates Reactive Oxygen Species (ROS) Generation by Leucocytes," *Journal of Clinical Endocrinology and Metabolism* 85.8 (2000): 2970–73.

(11) P. Riederer et al., "Advanced Glycation Endproducts Change Glutathione Redox Status in SH-SY5Y Human Neuroblastoma Cells by a Hydrogen-Peroxide-Dependent Mechanism," *Neuroscience Letters* 312.1 (2001): 29–32.

(12) M. H. Helmy et al., "Effect of Selenium Supplementation on the Activities of Glutathione-Metabolizing Enzymes in Human Hepatoma Hep G2 Cell Line," *Toxicology* (Amsterdam, Netherlands) 144.1–3 (2000): 57–61.

(13) T. Chepda et al., "Synergy Between Ascorbate and Alpha Tocopherol on Fibroblasts in Culture," *Life Sciences* 69.14 (2001): 1587–96.

(14) S. Khanna et al., "Alpha Lipoic Acid Supplementation: Tissue Glutathione Homeostasis at Rest and After Exercise,"

Journal of Applied Physiology 86.4 (1999): 1191–96.

(15) Mujgan Cengiz and Salih Cengiz, "The Effect of Vitamin C Administration on Erythrocyte Glutathione and HbA1c Levels of Type II Diabetic Patients," *Cerrahpasa Tp Dergisi* 31.4 (2000): 211–15.

BIBLIOGRAPHY—SCIENTIFIC REFERENCES

The content of *Your Dog's Health* is based on a body of scientific research which is detailed in *Potential Within: A Guide to Nutritional Empowerment*. *Potential Within* was inspired by personal trials and tribulations coupled to the scientific research I have been engaged in since 1992—nutrigenomics (nutrient-gene interactions) and how it relates to insulin health, diabetes, autoimmune and inflammatory disease. These studies began with a performance initiative and led to the investigation of therapeutic strategies which changed my life and the lives of others who applied the programs.

Potential Within discusses the science of nutrient-based ingredients and does not present brands or specific products. It provides the foundation knowledge needed to read labels and identify condition-and target-specific ingredients and their most effective forms. This guidance allows one to choose nutritional products and combinations of products which best treat conditions, promote maximum health benefit, preserve youth and generate powerful performance potential in sport. It also instils a thorough knowledge of the effect of foods, their timing and combinations; and it provides insight on lifestyle and how it influences hormones, metabolism, mood, health and disease. *Potential Within* teaches how to extract the healing, life and performance potential within all of us.

These formidable strategies were soon applied to improve the performance potential of my athlete companion animals; and eventually to heal and improve the lives of companion animals in distress. Much of our human health research stems from animal trials which made the administration of these natural remedies appropriate treatments for our pets once the suitable accommodations for the metabolic differences were considered. *Your Dog's Health* is founded by the work presented in *Potential Within*. *Potential Within* is designed to treat human health challenges and promote human wellness.

The relief experienced by our companion animals through this work is tear-jerking as life changing experiences pave new paths for the families involved. The results in our pets is also validation for known therapies and windows into new potential for human applications. The research continues with a focus on improving treatments for diabetes, arthritis, obesity, gastrointestinal disorders, skin disease and other inflammatory conditions in both human and companion animal populations.

The latest extremely exciting revelations have even opened windows into the regulation of autoimmune diseases; an escalating problem in our pet and human populations. This will change how disease is treated forever more since the immune component and its inflammatory chemistry is at the root of most chronic and acute diseases, autoimmune and other. The 680 scientific references displayed in the last fifty pages of *Potential Within* and the extensive work within the body of this 'mother information source' serve as the scientific evidence supporting *Your Dog's Health*. *Potential Within* is the information and reference source for the material in multiple subsequent books. To maintain the scientific credibility of *Potential Within*, specific product brands are not discussed in this book.

On the other hand, to make application of these strategies easy for pet guardians, the pet strategies have been formulated into products which are described in scientific detail in the latter pages of *Your Dog's Health*.

ISBN 0-9731701-0-07
Available in participating
Health Stores and Book Stores
Visit: *www.biologicnr.com*
for more information

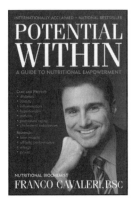

PROF. FRANCO CAVALERI, BSC, NB

Franco Cavaleri, a prominent nutritional biochemist, is the founder of **BiologicVET**™nutritional supplements for cats and dogs, and the author of the best-selling *Potential Within: A Guide To Nutritional Empowerment* and *Your Dog's Health.*

Cavaleri graduated from the University of British Columbia, where he majored in Nutritional Science and Biochemistry. His postgraduate work continues to focus on the latest gene-related and insulin-related nutraceutical research. His efforts in scientific research and development of nutrient-gene interactions have resulted in widespread recognition in the health industry, including Gold, Silver and Bronze Alive Formulation awards in addition to best-seller status for his book, *Potential Within*.

Your Dog's Health, is a reflection of Franco's research into pet health, a body of work which paralleled the research founding *Potential Within*, a book designed primarily with an objective to treat human health challenges and promote wellbeing for the human population. He is has completed a soon-to-be-published third book unveiling his research on nutrigenomic activity related to immune system empowerment and resolution and coping with autoimmunity; a fourth book relating to the psychological, emotional and physical dimensions of human wellness and how it relates to nutrition and nutrient-based (nutrigenomics) therapies.

He is a sought after consultant and speaker on human and pet health issues throughout North America and overseas. Franco lectures to pharmacy and other health care students of post secondary institutions introducing the pharmacology and drug interactions of nutraceuticals. He is also a frequent television guest and contributor to numerous magazines. Cavaleri's professional path was inspired by his own recovery from a life threatening disease, much to the amazement of medical professionals. His work has led to the development of powerful gene- and cytokine-modifying programs designed to treat autoimmune diseases naturally. With the belief that intelligent nutrition can be life-changing and metabolic correction the true treatment for disease, he has set out to share his message with consumers and health care professionals world wide.

A former soccer player and competitive bodybuilder, Cavaleri has won several titles including the pro-qualifier, IFBB North American Bodybuilding Championships in Los Angeles California. Today, he serves as CEO, president, and research director of Biologic Publishing Inc and Biological Nutrigenomics Health Research Corp. (*www.biologicnr.com*) and is an adviser to industry companies and organizations involved in human and animal nutrition. In April of 2004, Franco was inducted into the CHFA's Sports Nutrition Hall of Fame for his efforts and contributions to the health care and sports nutrition industries. He also sits on the board of the Canadian Sports Nutrition Association.

He has founded many corporations in the past twenty years, each revolving around human and animal performance and wellness— Champions Choice Advanced Nutrition and Biologic Nutritional Research Inc. These two companies have become part of corporate mergers while Cavaleri continues his work today through Biologic Publishing Inc. and Biologic Nutrigenomics Research Corp. (*www.biologicnr.com*)

Cavaleri and his lovely wife, Kimiko, are proud parents of two beautiful children and the guardians of three companion canines. He practices his health and wellness word and his family lives a 'Family Comes First' life plan. Franco also volunteers some time as a youth soccer coach.